FRENCH LANDSCAPE DRAWINGS AND SKETCHES OF THE EIGHTEENTH CENTURY

French Landscape Drawings and Sketches
of the Eighteenth Century

Catalogue
OF A LOAN EXHIBITION
FROM THE LOUVRE AND OTHER FRENCH MUSEUMS
AT THE
DEPARTMENT OF PRINTS AND DRAWINGS
IN THE BRITISH MUSEUM
1977

Published for the Trustees of the British Museum
BRITISH MUSEUM PUBLICATIONS LIMITED

Cover: Rome: the Tiber and St Peter's under a stormy sky,
by Pierre-Henri de Valenciennes (no. 135)

© 1977 THE TRUSTEES OF THE BRITISH MUSEUM

ISBN 0 7141 0761 1 cased

ISBN 0 7141 0762 X paper

Published by British Museum Publications Ltd,
6 Bedford Square, London WC1B 3RA

Designed by John Mitchell

Set in 10pt Garamond and printed in Great Britain by

Balding and Mansell Ltd, Wisbech and London

CONTENTS

PREFACE   7

INTRODUCTION   9

ALPHABETICAL LIST OF ARTISTS   15

BIBLIOGRAPHY OF WORKS REFERRED TO
IN ABBREVIATED FORM.   16

Catalogue.   19

PLATES   113

** An asterisk
below the catalogue number
denotes an illustration in
the plates section*

PREFACE

We do not immediately think of French eighteenth-century art in terms of landscape. For most people, the words 'French landscape' evoke either the seventeenth century or the nineteenth: either Claude and Poussin, or Corot, the Barbizon School, the Impressionists and Cézanne. Yet no one who saw the exhibition of the work of Joseph Vernet at Kenwood last summer can have doubted that the four great canvases from the series of *The Harbours of France*, which dates from the very middle of the eighteenth century, were the product of a living and deeply rooted tradition of landscape art. Roseline Bacou's suggestion that the Louvre's contribution to our proposed exchange should take this form was an inspired one, for in this country we are still inclined to think of landscape-drawing – especially in the eighteenth century – as something of an English monopoly. As she points out in her admirable introduction to the catalogue, the art of landscape in France has its roots in the Netherlandish seventeenth century: the tradition set by the group of Flemish painters and draughtsmen who worked for Louis XIV towards the end of the century was strengthened by the influence of the earlier landscape-painters of the Dutch school whose work particularly appealed to French eighteenth-century taste. Hence the first contrast between French and English landscape drawings to strike the visitor will probably be the obvious one of colour: with a few notable exceptions, such as Richard Wilson (whose drawing technique was in fact derived from French artists whom he met in Rome in the 1750's), Alexander Cozens and Gainsborough, the preferred medium of English landscape draughtsmen has always been watercolour; while their French counterparts have on the whole tended to follow their Netherlandish predecessors in the use of the traditional techniques of monochrome wash or chalk – either black or red – often on coloured paper. It may, nevertheless, come as a surprise to the English-watercolour-fancier to find Adam van der Meulen at the end of the seventeenth century or Jean-Pierre Houel in the 1770's using the medium with a delicacy and a mastery unsurpassed by any of their English contemporaries.

But French eighteenth-century landscape is not to be seen simply as an offshoot of the art of the Netherlands. If France's northern frontier is with Flanders, those to the south are with Italy and Spain, and French culture owes much of its exceptional richness and diversity to its balanced combination of northern and Latin elements. The realistic strain in French landscape, derived from the north, was complemented by an Italian – or, it would be more accurate to say, 'Italianate', since it stemmed principally from Claude and Poussin – tendency to idealization, which found full expression at the end of the century in the Neo-Classic conception of '*paysage composé*'. Even more pervasive was the influence of the landscape of Italy itself, and especially of Rome. In 1666 the French Academy in Rome was founded by Louis XIV, as part of his policy of centralizing the official organization of the arts in France, including artistic education; and by the early eighteenth century the 'voyage d'Italie' had become an essential part of the training of every French artist. The more talented or more fortunate achieved it under official auspices as *pensionnaires* of the Academy, but there were few aspiring young artists who did not by some means or another contrive to spend at least a year or two in Rome. It is only since 1871 that Rome has gradually ceased to be one of the most picturesquely beautiful cities in the world.

Throughout the eighteenth century the tradition of Claude and Poussin still lingered there. Its beauty must have had an overwhelming effect on the new arrivals, even if landscape was not their primary interest, and the successive Directors of the French Academy did everything in their power to encourage the *pensionnaires* and their friends to devote as much time as possible to sketching in the city or the surrounding *campagna*. It is significant that many drawings in the present exhibition are by artists whose real bent lay in the direction of decorative or history painting and whose interest in landscape was confined to their years in Rome. Significant too is the high proportion of minor artists represented. Watteau and Boucher are of course included, but their landscape drawings, beautiful as they are, represent an occasional distraction from their main preoccupation with figurative art; and it is true that Vernet, Fragonard and Hubert Robert are masters of at least comparable stature; but the stars of the exhibition are such relatively obscure personalities as Desportes, Houel and Valenciennes.

The theme of eighteenth-century French landscape drawing could not be treated adequately within strict chronological, or even technical, limits. Two drawings by Adam van der Meulen (d. 1690) and one by Israel Silvestre (d. 1691) have been included to illustrate the Flemish origin of the early eighteenth-century style; also two by Pierre Patel (d. 1676) which represent the alternative 'classical' tradition of Claude and Poussin in the conventionalized and watered-down form which its later imitators found assimilable. At the other extreme, there are drawings by Michallon (d. 1822), George Michel (d. 1843) and Granet (d. 1849), all of whom continued the eighteenth-century tradition until well into the next century.

The inclusion of two groups of sketches in oil on paper, by François Desportes (d. 1743) and Pierre-Henri de Valenciennes (d. 1819), may seem an anomaly in an exhibition of drawings, but sketches of this kind represent an important and influential aspect of the French landscape tradition. Their authors did not look upon them as finished works, and, indeed, they served exactly the same purpose as sketches on paper in chalk or wash; but since they are in a medium associated with painting and not with drawing they have been relegated to limbo as being neither one thing nor the other, and as a result have never been adequately studied. For a painter like Valenciennes, whose finished landscapes were formal compositions devised according to the Neo-Classic theory of '*paysage composé*' or '*paysage historique*', sketching directly from nature provided the continuous and intimate contact with reality that was essential if his work was not to degenerate into conventionalism; and to this practice is due the presence, in even the most 'artificial' of his Salon pictures, of many beautifully observed and beautifully rendered passages of natural description. For the landscape painters of a later generation the practice of *plein-air* sketching in this way ceased to be necessary. By the middle of the nineteenth century the shift of taste had occurred that saw in the spontaneity and freshness of the sketch the qualities to be looked for in the finished picture – as we see in the paintings of the Impressionists and their forerunners of the Barbizon School.

It is a particular pleasure to welcome this loan exhibition from the Cabinet des Dessins of the Louvre, both for its own sake and as a practical expression of the long-standing and close relationship between our two institutions. Particular thanks are due to Roseline Bacou, to whose imagination and energy the exhibition owes respectively its conception and its realization, and to Maurice Sérullaz, Conservateur en chef du Cabinet des Dessins, for his unfailing support. I have also to thank Martin Kisch, Research Assistant in the Department, for his assistance with the translation and production of the catalogue.

J. A. GERE *Keeper of Prints and Drawings*

INTRODUCTION

This exhibition represents one half of an exchange between the Louvre and the British Museum. For the first time a group of works from French public collections are being shown in the gallery of the Department of Prints and Drawings; a year later, in the Autumn of 1978, a choice of the British Museum's collection of drawings by Claude Lorrain will in turn be shown in the Pavillon de Flore. Such an agreement could not have been reached without the existence over the past thirty years of a particularly close relationship between the Cabinet des Dessins and the staff of the Department of Prints and Drawings, especially the three Keepers of the Department during that period, the late A. E. Popham, (whom it is a particular pleasure for us to commemorate) and his two successors, Mr Croft-Murray and Mr Gere, and also Mr Philip Pouncey, formerly Deputy Keeper.

Our choice of subject was prompted by the fact that English artists and collectors have always been particularly interested in landscape. The Royal Academy winter exhibition of 1949–50, *Landscape in French Art*, had comprehensively illustrated the development of the art of landscape in France from the middle of the sixteenth century; but it seemed to us that an exhibition limited to drawings, and to drawings of a single period, would constitute a significant complement to its predecessor by enabling one aspect of the subject to be studied in detail. We have not tried to trace the historic evolution of landscape in all its aspects, so much as to illustrate the reaction of the artist when confronted by nature, as he conveys, with a spontaneity made possible by the medium of drawing (and by this term is included here the oil-sketch on paper) the freshness of his first impressions. I hope that the choice of drawings, for which I was responsible in consultation with John Gere and Maurice Sérullaz, Conservateur en chef of the Cabinet des Dessins, has fulfilled this aim. The names of Fragonard and Hubert Robert are often cited as typifying the French landscape of the eighteenth century, but the present large representation of Desportes, Oudry, Natoire, Blarenberghe, Houel and Valenciennes, to say nothing of such lesser draughtsmen as Portail, Pierre, Vien, Challe, Suvée, Perignon, Bidault and Constantin, will we hope, lead to a broader view of the eighteenth-century conception of 'pure landscape'; and thus to a closer understanding of this period of French art, which, paradoxically, is one of the best known and also one of the least well understood.

In the seventeenth century, landscape was not considered a particularly elevated branch of painting. It was appreciated only in so far as it served as the setting for some human activity. As late as 1719, in his 'Critical Reflections on Poetry and Painting', the Abbé Dubos could write: 'The most beautiful landscape, even by Titian or Carracci, is of no more interest to us than an actual tract of country, which may be either hideous or pleasant. Such a painting contains nothing which, as it were, speaks to us; and since we are not moved by it, we do not find it of any particular interest. Intelligent artists have always been so well aware of this truth that they have rarely painted landscapes without figures.' Fortunately, more licence was permitted in drawings, but it is significant that the leading landscape artists in France in the seventeenth century made drawings on the spot not as ends in themselves but in preparation for some more elaborate work. Thus Israel Silvestre's remarkable watercolours of the Flemish towns recaptured by Louis XIV were made for engravings; while Adam van der Meulen accompanied the King on his campaigns and studied the landscape of the battlefields in order to give the greatest possible verisimilitude to his tapestry cartoons. The significance of tapestry in the development of landscape cannot be overlooked. Van der Meulen played a large part in the design of the series of the *Seasons* and the *Histoire du Roy*, Patel in that of *Les Maisons Royales*, both for Louis XIV; in the eighteenth century landscape played an even larger part in tapestry design, which explains why so much of the activity of Desportes, Oudry, Boucher, Natoire and even Pillement, was involved with the Gobelins and Beauvais factories.

French landscape in the seventeenth century was deeply affected by Flemish influences. We need only recall the presence in Paris from 1621 onwards of Rubens's collaborator, the landscape painter Jacques Foucquier, and of the many Flemish artists who were later brought together by van der Meulen to assist him at the Gobelins. In the eighteenth century these influences inclined artists in the direction of a greater truth to nature and a more realistic use of colour. From the beginning of the century, some draughtsmen, like Watteau, used the technique of red chalk, and others, like Oudry, watercolour, often on coloured paper. Desportes, who through his master Bernaert was a pupil at one remove of Snyders, used oil on paper for his sketches after nature of landscape and plants. Collectors and artists continued their interest in Dutch and Flemish landscape until the very end of the century, as we see from contemporary sale catalogues. P.-J. Mariette, whose collection was sold in 1775, did not conceal his preference for the Italian school, but he also brought together a fine collection of Netherlandish drawings; in the provinces, the landscape paintings by Dutch and Flemish artists that T. A. Desfriches collected at Orléans were the direct inspiration of his own drawings; and the same was true of Saint-Morys, whose important collection of drawings was acquired by the Louvre as a result of the Revolution. The same influence is reflected, to a greater or lesser extent, by most of the artists in this exhibition, by Oudry and Boucher and even to some extent by Fragonard, who visited Holland in 1772; while in the last quarter of the eighteenth century we find artists of independent temperament, like Boissieu and Georges Michel, following the inspiration of Dutch seventeenth-century landscape in their own directly observed down-to-earth records of the everyday aspects of nature. Watteau's development is more complicated. From his Flemish origin he derives his interest in nature and his taste for drawing directly from it – we know that he made sketches out of doors at Montmorency, in the suburb of Porcherons and at Nogent-sur-Marne – but he had other sources of inspiration, in particular the Venetian masters of the early sixteenth century, of whose pen and ink drawings, which he saw in the house of his friend and patron Crozat and in the Royal Collection, he made copies in red chalk. It is due to him that landscape became one of the essential features of the *fête galante*; his figures and the natural settings in which he placed them show a high degree of idealization founded on a basis of the most exact observation. The concept of the *fête galante* underwent many variations at the hands of his followers, and persisted in spite of all changes of taste: there is an echo of it even at the height of the Neo-Classic vogue, in the views of gardens animated by strolling figures drawn by Moreau l'aîné or Norblin de la Gourdaine.

Contemporary accounts occasionally provide a glimpse of the eighteenth-century artist sketching from nature: in a letter of 1720 to Julienne, Watteau writes of 'the landscapes of Nogent of which you must be particularly fond, since it was in the company of Madame de Julienne that I made the first sketches for them'. Desportes, so we are told by his nephew, 'on his walks in the country carried, in tin boxes, his brushes and his palette ready prepared . . . and he used a small metal easel which could be screwed into the head of his walking stick; he never went to stay with friends in the country without taking with him this easily portable equipment'. The phrase 'after nature' occurs for the first time in the catalogues of the Salon with reference to landscapes by Oudry, of whom the Abbé Goujenot wrote, in 1761, that 'on Sundays and holidays his greatest pleasure was to go to the Forest of Saint Germain or to Chantilly or to the Bois du Bougeon, in order to make studies of tree-trunks, plants, woodland vistas, stormy skies, horizons'. Goujenot also described the garden at Arcueil, the neglected state of which was an additional beauty in the eyes of artists, and which had attracted not only Oudry but also Natoire, Boucher and Portail: 'everywhere one came across people sketching, all anxious to ask advice from M. Oudry, who in this picturesque pastime appeared like a schoolmaster among his pupils'. Goujenot's words were well chosen, for by about 1740 landscape sketching out of doors had indeed become the pastime of Parisian artists. Young artists were also given the opportunity of visiting Italy. There, with pencil in hand, they discovered new subjects, and by mixing with the foreign artists in Rome they came to realise the increasing importance attached to landscape in Europe as a whole.

Joseph Vernet spent the years from 1734 to 1753 in Rome, and from 1751 to 1774 Charles-Joseph Natoire was Director of the French Academy there. The influence of the active studio which Vernet maintained in Rome during those twenty years, and the role of Natoire in encouraging his *pensionnaires* to sketch directly from nature, are both well known. Interest in landscape seems to have been a common feature of the many complex artistic currents of which Rome was then the meeting place. We find it for example in the paintings of Panini and the etchings of Piranesi; in the development of view-painting to satisfy the demands of wealthy travellers on the Grand Tour; in the discovery by archaeological draughtsmen of the beauty of unfamiliar countries; and in the beginning of the fashion for topographical literature in the form of illustrated guide-books and accounts of picturesque travel. This interest was a fundamental one with the young French artists in Rome all of whom without exception made drawings from nature during their time there. Some of them, like the architect Legeay and the painters Pierre, Suvée and Vien, treated it merely as an exercise, while others, such as Fragonard, Robert, Lallemand, Houel, Amand or Nicolle, were led to discover their vocation as landscape artists.

It was not long before French collectors developed a taste for work of this kind. The feeling for nature which originated among the intellectual *élite* quickly spread to a wider public. The success of literary works like the *Spectacle of Nature* by the Abbé Pluche in 1732 and Thomson's *Seasons* in 1730 foreshadows the effect on French sensibility of Rousseau's *Nouvelle Héloïse* (1761), Solomon Gessner's pastoral *Idyllen*, translated from the German in 1762, and Jean-François de Saint-Lambert's *Saisons* (1769). Drawings of landscape began to appear in exhibitions. In the Salon of 1765, for example, Fragonard exhibited the red chalk drawings of Tivoli which he had just brought back from Rome. The rediscovery of the 'joys of nature' stimulated the renewal of the art of landscape gardening, in which Watelet and Robert took a leading part. It also stimulated travel. Frontiers have never been more lightly crossed than by the French artists of the eighteenth century. Italy was not their only goal: Fragonard, Le Prince and Desfriches all went to the Netherlands; Vernet and Pérignon to Switzerland; Pillement and Noël to Spain and Portugal; Le Prince to Russia; Deprez to Sweden; Norblin and Pillement to Poland; London also attracted many French artists, beginning with Watteau in 1719.

Views drawn on the spot were engraved to illustrate books of travel: Fragonard, Robert, Chatelet, Desprez and Pâris were among those who contributed to Saint-Non's famous *Voyage pittoresque . . . de Naples et de Sicile* (1781–86); Houel published his own illustrated *Voyage pittoresque des Isles de Sicile, de Lipari et de Malte* between 1783 and 1787; from 1784 onwards Cassas was making drawings to illustrate Choiseul-Gouffier's *Voyage pittoresque de la Grèce*, and later published illustrated volumes dealing with his own travels in the Near East (1799), Istria and Dalmatia (1800), Greece, Sicily and Rome (1813). Their interest was not confined to antique remains, historical sites and local customs: it extended to natural curiosities, ranging from the volcanic phenomena which Boissieu studied in the Auvergne in 1766 and Houel in Sicily and Lipari between 1776 and 1779, to the Alpine glaciers represented in Laborde and Zurlauben's *Tableau Topographique, pittoresques, physiques . . . de la Suisse* (1780–6). Draughtsmen also accompanied scientific expeditions like those of the astronomer, the Abbé Chappe, who took Noël to Southern California in 1768. To the draughtsmen of the second half of the century, we owe the discovery of the landscape of France itself. Immediately after his return from Rome in 1753, Joseph Vernet, accompanied by his assistant Nicolas Ozanne, travelled all over the country in connection with his series of paintings of *The Harbours of France*, and in 1776 L. N. van Blarenberghe devoted a whole series of watercolours to the harbour of Brest. Houel, Pérignon and Noël worked in Normandy; Desfriches in the region of Orléans; Boissieu in the country round Lyons; David de Marseille and Constantin in Provence; Bidault anticipated the interest of nineteenth-century artists in Fontainebleau, Brittany and The Dauphiné. J. B. Laborde's publication, *Voyage pittoresque de la France*, the first volume of which appeared in 1781, sent artists into the provinces in search of subject matter. Lallemand, for example, went to Burgundy and the Franche-Comté. Paris itself, with its monuments and gardens, its new streets and buildings, was for Lespinasse, De Machy, Nicolle and the Saint-Aubin brothers an inexhaustible subject, as were the parks and gardens of the Ile de France for Moreau l'aîné and, at the beginning of the next century, the suburbs of Paris for Georges Michel. Though these draughtsmen sometimes used black chalk and brown and grey wash, their favourite techniques were watercolour or gouache which were more suited to render the freshness of outdoor light. The place and the date are often inscribed on the drawing, and sometimes (as for example in those by Wille) the time of day and the state of the weather. At the bottom of his panoramic view of Paris, the *tour-de-force* which Lespinasse presented as his *morceau de réception* on his election to the Academy in 1787, the artist has even noted that the drawing reproduces the light of 'between eleven o'clock and noon'. In the last quarter of the century, David's rigorous interpretation of the principles of Neo-Classicism tended to divert the ambitions of French artists into other channels than the mere reproduction of the beauties of nature; but it is significant that Valenciennes, the leading exponent of the Neo-Classic theory of '*paysage historique*', and his pupil Michallon, the first winner of the Prix de Rome for Historical Landscape which was established in 1816 largely through the efforts of Valenciennes, should both have made oil-sketches of 'pure landscape' which anticipate the early work of Michallon's pupil Corot.

Another of the influences that helped to free French artists from an unduly theoretical approach and encouraged them towards a greater directness of expression was that of English art. Artistic exchanges between England and France were frequent in the eighteenth century: Desportes came to London in 1712 and Watteau in 1719–20; Gravelot settled there from 1732 to 1745, during which time Gainsborough frequented his studio. Paul Sandby in London was influenced by the watercolours of Chatelain and Goupy, while in Rome Alexander Cozens and Thomas Patch were pupils of Vernet, and it was Vernet who encouraged Richard Wilson to devote himself to landscape. He also had some influence upon Thomas Marlowe, who after Italy spent some time in south-eastern France. Pillement worked for ten years in England from 1750 to 1760, while Legeay came to London in 1768, three years before Clérisseau who had been the companion and teacher of Robert Adam in Italy and was to collaborate in many of his decorative schemes. Philip de Loutherbourg, a native of Lorraine who was elected a member of the Académie Royale in Paris in 1766, enjoyed a successful career as a landscape artist in England from 1771 onwards and even encouraged the youthful Turner. Exchanges of this kind, though interrupted by the Revolutionary wars, were resumed after the conclusion of peace and opened a way for the discovery of English painting, and especially of the landscape watercolour, which was to be so decisive for French artists in the decade after 1815.

The majority of the drawings exhibited come from the Cabinet des Dessins of the Louvre, but in order to make the representation of some artists more complete, and also to associate other institutions with this first loan exhibition to the British Museum, we have drawn on certain collections in Paris and elsewhere that are especially rich in eighteenth-century drawings. We gratefully acknowledge the generous help and collaboration of M. Michel Laclotte, Conservateur en chef of the Department of Paintings of the Louvre; M. Jean-Marie Moulin, Conservateur en chef of the Musée de Compiègne; M. Jean Mathieu and Mme Préau, respectively Director and Librarian of the Manufacture de Sèvres; M. Bernard de Montgolfier, Conservateur en chef of the Musée Carnavalet; Mme Adeline Cacan de Bissy, Conservateur en chef of the Musée du Petit Palais; Mlle Jacques, of the Library of the Ecole des Beaux-Arts; M. Carlos van Hasselt, Director of the Fondation Custodia of the Dutch Institute in Paris; Mlle Olga Popovitch of the Rouen Museum; M. Daniel Ojalvo of the Orléans Museum and M. Denis Coutagne of the Besançon Museum.

The catalogue has been compiled by myself (nos. 1–5, 18–20, 30, 32, 45–53, 61–2, 69, 79–84, 98–114, 121–2, 125–6, 149–52), Lise Duclaux, Conservateur au Cabinet des Dessins (nos. 6–17, 22–9, 31, 33–9, 42–4, 54, 58, 63, 72, 75, 117–20, 130–47) and Jean-François Méjanès, Conservateur au Cabinet des Dessins et à la Chalcographie du Louvre (nos. 40–1, 46, 55–7, 59–60, 64–8, 70–1, 73–4, 76–8, 85–97, 115–16, 123–4, 127–9, 148, 153–5).

The translation into English and the revision and editing of the text, were undertaken by Mr Gere, to whom we are also indebted for many valuable suggestions.

ROSELINE BACOU
Conservateur en chef au Cabinet des Dessins

ALPHABETICAL LIST OF ARTISTS INCLUDED

AMAND, Jacques-François   nos. 76–78

BELANGER, Louis   no. 115

BIDAULD, François-Xavier   no. 148

BLARENBERGHE, Louis-Nicolas and Henri-Joseph   nos. 47–53

BOISSIEU, Jean-Jacques de   nos. 113–114

BOUCHER, François   nos. 37–39

CASSAS, Louis-François   nos. 143–145

CHALLE, Michel-Ange   no. 56

CHATELET, Claude-Louis   no. 129

CLERISSEAU   no. 59

CONSTANTIN, Jean-Antoine   nos. 146–147

DAVID, Jacques-Louis   no. 128

DAVID, Joseph-Antoine called de Marseille   no. 63

DEMACHY, Pierre-Antoine   no. 61

DESFRICHES, Aignan-Thomas   no. 45

DESPORTES, François   nos. 6–17

DESPREZ, Louis-Jean   no. 122

FRAGONARD, Jean-Honoré   nos. 79–84

GILLOT, Claude   no. 18

GRANET, François-Marius   nos. 151–152

HOUEL, Jean   nos. 101–112

LALLEMAND, Jean-Baptiste   no. 54

LANTARA, Simon-Mathurin   nos. 73–74

LE BARBIER, Jean-Jacques   no. 116

LE GEAY, Jean-Laurent   no. 40

LE METTAY, Pierre-Charles   no. 64

LEMPEREUR, Jean-Baptiste-Denis   no. 69

LE PRINCE, Jean-Baptiste   nos. 96–97

LESPINASSE, Louis-Nicolas de   nos. 98–100

MARIETTE, Pierre-Jean   no. 30

MEULEN, Adam Franz van der   nos. 4–5

MICHALLON, Achille-Etna   nos. 153–155

MICHEL, Georges   nos. 149–150

MOITTE, Pierre-Etienne   no. 60

MOREAU, Louis-Gabriel   nos. 117–120

NATOIRE, Charles-Joseph   nos. 33–36

NICOLLE, Victor-Jean   no. 142

NOEL, Alexandre-Jean   no. 141

NORBLIN DE LA GOURDAINE, Jean-Pierre   nos. 125–126

OUDRY, Jacques-Charles   no. 58

OUDRY, Jean-Baptiste   nos. 22–29

OZANNE, Nicolas-Marie   no. 72

PARIS, Pierre-Adrien   no. 124

PATEL, Pierre   nos. 1, 2

PERIGNON, Nicolas   nos. 65–68

PIERRE, Jean-Baptiste Marie   no. 41

PILLEMENT, Jean   nos. 70–71

PORTAIL, Jacques-André   no. 31

ROBERT, Hubert   nos. 85–95

SAINT-AUBIN, Gabriel de   no. 62

SAINT-MORYS   no. 121

SILVESTRE, Israël   no. 3

SILVESTRE, Nicolas-Charles   no. 32

SUVEE, Joseph-Benoit   no. 123

VALENCIENNES, Pierre-Henri de   nos. 130–140

VERNET, Joseph   nos. 42–44

VIEN, Joseph-Marie   no. 55

VINCENT, François-André   no. 127

VOLAIRE, Pierre-Jacques   no. 75

WATELET, Claude-Henri   no. 57

WATTEAU, Antoine   nos. 19–21

WILLE, Jean-Georges   no. 46

WORKS REFERRED TO IN ABBREVIATED FORM

Abecedario — *Abecedario de P.-J. Mariette et autres notes inédites de cet amateur sur les arts et les artistes. Ouvrage publié d'après les manuscrits autographes conservés au Cabinet des Estampes de la Bibliothèque Impériale et annoté*, par Ph. de Chennevières et A. de Montaiglon. Paris, 1851–60, 6 vols.

Adhémar, 1950 — H. Adhémar, *Watteau, sa vie, son oeuvre*, Paris, 1950.

Ananoff — A. Ananoff, *L'Oeuvre dessiné de Jean-Honoré Fragonard*, Paris, I, 1961; II, 1963; III, 1968; IV, 1970.

Ananoff, 1966 — A. Ananoff, *L'oeuvre dessiné de François Boucher (1703–1770). Catalogue raisonné*, Paris, I, 1966.

Ananoff, 1976 — A. Ananoff, *François Boucher*, Paris, 1976.

Audin and Vial, 1918–19 — M. Audin et E. Vial, *Dictionnaire des artistes et ouvriers d'art en France: Lyonnais*, Paris, 1918–19.

Babelon, 1970 — J. P. Babelon, 'Le Palais de l'Arsenal à Paris, Etudes architecturales et essai de répertoire iconographique critique', *Bulletin Monumental*, 1970, pp. 287 ff.

Bacou, 1971 — R. Bacou, *Il settecento francese*, Milan, 1971

Bacou, 1976 — R. Bacou, 'Bolognese Drawings of the Seventeenth Century', *Apollo*, CIV, November 1976, pp. 382–87, and *Treasures from the Lugt Collection*, London, 1976, pp. 124–29.

Batowski, 1911 — Z. Batowski, *J. P. Norblin*, Lwow, 1911.

Bean, 1964 — J. Bean, 'French Drawings in Dutch Collections', *Master Drawings*, 2, 1964, no. 3, pp. 293–96.

Beau, 1968 — M. Beau, *La Collection des dessins d'Hubert Robert au Musée de Valence*, Lyon, 1968.

Benard, 1810 — M. Benard, *Cabinet de M. Paignon-Dijonval*, Paris, 1810.

Benisovich, 1952 — M. Benisovich, 'Quelques artistes français au Portugal', *Gazette des Beaux-Arts*, 1952, I, pp. 115 ff.

Berckenhagen, 1970 — E. Berckenhagen, *Die Französischen Zeichnungen der Kunstbibliothek Berlin*, Berlin, 1970.

Bergsträsser, 1970 — G. Bergsträsser, 'Zeichnungen von J. J. de Boissieu im Hessischen Landesmuseum zu Darmstadt', *Kunst in Hessen und am Mittelrhein*, 10, 1970, pp. 89–99.

Blanc, 1857 — Ch. Blanc, *Trésor de la curiosité*, Paris, 1857.

Bonnardot, 1857 — Bonnardot, 'Iconographie de vieux Paris', *Revue Universelle des Arts*, v, 1857, pp. 25, 210, 402.

Boucher, 1923 — H. Boucher, 'V. J. Nicolle 1754–1826', *Gazette des Beaux-arts*, 1923, I, pp. 97–113.

Boucher, 1925 — F. Boucher, 'Le Pont-Neuf' dans *Gazette-des-Beaux-arts*, 1925, I.

Boucher, 1926 — H. Boucher, 'Louis-François Cassas', *Gazette des Beaux-arts*, 1926, II, pp. 27 ff, 209 ff.

Boucher and Jaccottet, 1952 — F. Boucher et Ph. Jaccottet, *Le Dessin français au XVIIIe siècle*, Lausanne, 1952

Bouillon-Landais, 1952 — Bouillon-Landais, 'David de Marseille', *Réunion des Sociétés des Beaux-arts des départements*, 1893, pp. 371 ff.

Bourin, 1910 — H. Bourin, 'Le Chevalier de Lespinasse', *Bulletin de Société d'iconographie parisienne*, 1910, Paris, p. 25 ff.

Boyer, 1949 — F. Boyer, 'Catalogue raisonné de l'oeuvre de Charles Natoire', *Archives de l'art français*, 1949, pp. 32–106.

Cailleux, 1960 — J. Cailleux, 'An unpublished painting by Saint-Aubin: Le Bal Champêtre', *L'Art du Dix-huitième siècle*, no. 3, an advertisement supplement to the *Burlington Magazine*, CII 1960, pp. I–V.

Cailleux, 1969 — J. Cailleux, 'Hubert Robert, dessinateur de la Rome vivante 1757–1765', *Actes du Congrès international d'Histoire de l'Art*, pp. 57–61, Budapest, 1969.

Cailleux, 1975 — J. Cailleux, 'Hubert Robert's submissions to the Salon of 1769', *L'Art du Dix-huitième Siècle*; no. 32, an advertisement supplement to the Burlington Magazine, October 1975, pp. I–XVI.

Carlson, 1966 — V. Carlson, 'Three drawings by François Boucher', *Master Drawings*, 4, 1966, 2, pp. 157–63.

Chennevières, 1894–97 — Ph. de Chennevières, 'Une collection de dessins', *L'Artiste*, 1894–97.

Chennevières, 1898 — Ph. de Chennevières, 'Portail', *Gazette des Beaux-arts*, April 1898, I, pp. 315–30.

Chudant, 1929 — A. Chudant, *Catalogue des peintures et dessins du Musée de Besançon*, Besançon, 1929.

Cormack, 1970 — Malcolm Cormack, *The Drawings of Watteau*, London, 1970.

Cornillot, 1957 — *Inventaire général des Dessins des Musées de Province. I. Collection Pierre-Adrien Pâris, Besançon*, par M. L. Cornillot, Paris, 1957.

Correspondance des Directeurs — *Correspondance des Directeurs de l'Académie de France à Rome avec les Surintendants des Bâtiments, publiée d'après les manuscrits des Archives Nationales*, par A. de Montaiglon et J. Guiffrey, Paris, 1887–1912, 17 vols.

Dacier, 1929 — E. Dacier, *Gabriel de Saint-Aubin*, Paris, 1929, 2 vols.

Dacier, 1930 — E. Dacier, *Dessins de Maîtres français*, x. *52 dessins d'Antoine Watteau*, Paris, 1930.

David, 1880 — J. L. J. David, *Le Peintre Louis David (1748–1825) Souvenirs et documents inédits*, Paris, 1880.

Davoust, 1891 — G. Davoust, *Le Comte de Bizemont. Son oeuvre et ses collections*, Orléans, 1891.

Demonts, 1913 — L. Demonts, 'Notes sur les collections royales de peinture', *Bulletin de la Société de l'Histoire de l'Art français*, 1913, pp. 79–84.

Desguines, 1950 — A. Desguines, *L'oeuvre de J. B. Oudry sur le Parc et les jardins d'Arcueil*, Paris, 1950.

Dubled — H. Dubled, 'Album de dessins de J. A. P. Bidault', *Revue du Louvre*, 1972, pp. 387–88.

Duclaux, 1968 — *Dessins du Louvre, Ecoles françaises*, by M. Serullaz, L. Duclaux et G. Monnier, Paris, 1968.

Duclaux, 1975 — *Inventaire général des dessins. Ecole française*. XII, *Nadar–Ozanne*, par L. Duclaux, avec la participation de Anne Prache, Paris, 1975.

Dumesnil, 1858 — J. Dumesnil, *Histoire des plus célèbres amateurs français*, t.III: *Correspondance de Thomas Desfriches*, Paris, 1858.

16

Dussieux, Soulié, Chennevières, 1854 — Mémoires inédits sur la vie et les ouvrages des membres de l'Académie royale de peinture et de sculpture, publiés d'après les manuscrits conservés à l'Ecole impériale des Beaux-Arts, par L. Dussieux, E. Soulié, Ph. de Chennevières, Paul Mantz, A. de Montaiglon, Paris, 1854, 2 vols.

Eidelberg, 1967 — Martin P. Eidelberg, 'Watteau's Use of Landscape Drawings', Master Drawings, 5, 1967, 2, pp. 173–81.

Feuillet, 1926 — H. Feuillet, Les Dessins de Fragonard et d'Hubert Robert aux Musée et Bibliothèque de Besançon, Paris, 1926.

Focillon, 1918 — H. Focillon, Giovanni-Battista Piranesi, Paris, 1918.

Fontaine, 1910 — A. Fontaine, Les Collections de l'Académie Royale, Paris, 1910.

Fontaine, Caylus, 1910 — Comte de Caylus, Vies d'artistes du XVIIIè siècle ... publié avec une introduction et des notes par A. Fontaine, Paris, 1910.

Fournier-Sarlovèze, 1904 — Fournier-Sarlovèze, 'Les Peintres de Stanislas Auguste J. P. Norblin', Revue de l'Art Ancien et Moderne, 1904, II, pp. 279 ff.

Furcy-Raynaud — M. Furcy-Raynaud, 'Les tableaux et objets d'art saisis chez les Emigrés ...', Archives de l'Art français, 1912, pp. 245–343.

Gabillot, 1895 — C. Gabillot, Hubert Robert et son temps, Paris, 1895.

Ganay, 1935 — E. de Ganay, 'Les Jardins de Ménars', Revue de l'Art ancien et moderne, XVII, 1935, p. 157 ff.

Granges de Surgères, 1898 — Marquis de Granges de Surgères, 'Les artistes nantais. Notes et documents inédits. Portail', Nouvelles Archives de l'art français, 1898.

Grüber, 1973 — A. Ch. Grüber, 'L'oeuvre de P.A. Pâris à la Cour de France, 1779–1891', Bulletin de la Société de l'Histoire de l'Art français, 1973, pp. 213–22.

Guiffrey-Marcel — Inventaire général des dessins du Musée du Louvre et du Musée de Versailles. Ecole française, par J. Guiffrey et P. Marcel, I, 1907 (2ᵉed. 1933); II, 1908; III, 1909; IV, 1909; V, 1910; VI, 1911; VII, 1912; X, 1928.

Hadeln, 1924 — D. von Hadeln, Zeichnungen des Tizian, Berlin, 1924.

Hillemacher, 1877 — F. Hillemacher, Catalogue des estampes qui composent l'oeuvre de J. F. Norblin, peintre français, Paris, 1877.

Hourticq, 1920 — L. Hourticq, 'L'atelier de François Desportes', Gazette des Beaux-Arts, 1920, II, pp. 117 ff.

Ingersoll-Smouse, 1926 — F. Ingersoll-Smouse, Joseph Vernet, peintre de marine, Paris, 1926.

Jarry, 1928 — P. Jarry, 'Une précision sur Claude-Louis Chatelet', Bulletin de la Société de l'Histoire de l'Art français, 1928, pp. 351–52.

Jean-Richard, 1971 — P. Jean-Richard, 'Boucher, Gravures et Dessins', La Revue du Louvre, 1971, no. 3, 195 ff.

Kochatzky, Oberhuber et Knab — W. Koschatzky, K. Oberhuber et E. Knab, I grandi disegni italiani dell'Albertina di Vienna, Milan, 1972.

Lapauze, 1907 — H. Lapauze, Catalogue sommaire des collections Dutuit, Paris, 1907.

Lapauze, Gronkowski, Fauchier-Magnan, 1925 — H. Lapauze, C. Gronkowski, A. Fauchier-Magnan, Catalogue sommaire des collections Dutuit, Paris, 1925.

Lavallée, 1928 — P. Lavallée, Dessins français du XVIIIè siècle à l'Ecole des Beaux-Arts, Paris, 1928.

Lavallée, 1938 — P. Lavallée, J. H. Fragonard, quatorze dessins du Louvre, Paris, 1938.

Lavallée, 1948 — P. Lavallée, Le Dessin français, Paris, 1948.

Lechevallier-Chevignard, 1920 — G. Lechevallier-Chevignard, 'L'atelier de François Desportes', Revue de l'Art ancien et moderne, 1920, pp. 164 ff.

Leclere, 1913 — T. Leclere, Hubert Robert et les paysagistes français du XVIIIè siècle, Paris, 1913.

Locquin, 1912 — J. Locquin, Catalogue raisonné de l'oeuvre de J. B. Oudry, Paris, 1912.

Lossky, 1962 — B. Lossky, Inventaire des collections publiques françaises. Tours. Peintures du XVIIIè siècle, Paris, 1962.

Lugt — F. Lugt, Les Marques de Collections de dessins et d'estampes, Amsterdam, 1921; Supplément, The Hague, 1956.

Lugt, 1949 — F. Lugt, Musée du Louvre, Inventaire général des Dessins des Ecoles du Nord. Ecole flamande, Paris, 1949, 2 vols.

Magnin, 1929 — J. Magnin, Les dessins du XVIIIè siècle au Musée de Besançon, Dijon, 1929.

Martine, 1927 — Ch. Martine, Dessins de Maîtres Français. Fragonard, Paris, 1927.

Méjanès, 1969 — J. F. Méjanès, L'Académie de France à Rome sous J. Natoire. Inventaires des dessins des pensionnaires sous les directorats de N. Vleughels et J. F. Detroy (1725–1751) dans les collections publiques françaises. Typewritten thesis, Paris, Ecole du Louvre, 1969.

Méjanès, 1976 — J. F. Méjanès, 'A spontaneous feeling for nature. French Eighteenth-century landscape Drawings', Apollo, CIV, November 1976, pp. 396–404 and Treasures from the Lugt Collection, London, 1976, pp. 138 ff.

Michel, 1906 — E. Michel, Les Maîtres du Paysage, Paris, 1906.

Muraro and Rosand, 1976 — M. Muraro et D. Rosand, Tiziano e la silografia veneziana del Cinque-cento, Vicenza, 1976.

Nolhac, Loukomski, 1930 — P. de Nolhac et G. K. Loukomski, La Rome d'Hubert Robert, Paris, 1930.

Opperman, 1972 — H. N. Opperman, J. B. Oudry, with a sketch for a catalogue raisonné of his paintings, drawings and prints, doctoral thesis, University of Chicago, 1972, to be published.

Palluchini, 1969 — R. Palluchini, Tiziano, Florence, 1969, 2 vols.

Pâris, 1806 — 'Catalogue de mes livres, ainsi que des autres objets qui composent mon cabinet ...' par P. A. Pâris, 1806, MS, Bibliothèque Municipale de Besançon.

Parker, 1931 — K. T. Parker, The Drawings of Antoine Watteau, London, 1931.

Parker, 1938 — K. T. Parker, Catalogue of the Collection of drawings in the Ashmolean Museum, I, Oxford, 1938.

Parker and Mathey — K. T. Parker and J. Mathey, Antoine Watteau, catalogue complet de son oeuvre dessiné, Paris, 1957, 2 vols.

Parrocel, 1890 — E. Parrocel, Histoire documentaire de l'Académie de peinture et de sculpture de Marseille, Paris, 1889–80, 2 vols.

Pillement, 1945 — Georges Pillement, Jean Pillement, Paris, 1945.

Populus, 1930 — B. Populus, Claude Gillot. Catalogue de l'oeuvre gravé, Paris, 1930.

Portalis, 1889 — Baron R. Portalis, Honoré Fragonard, sa vie et son oeuvre, Paris, 1889.

Prache, 1975 — Voir Duclaux, 1975.

Ouglov and Roche, 1925 — L. Ouglov and D. Roche, 'Les dessins de Hoüel', La Renaissance de l'art français, December 1925, pp. 577 ff.

Quignon, 1920 — H. Quignon, 'La révélation de l'atelier de François Desportes', La Renaissance de l'art français, September 1920, pp. 353 ff.

Ratouis de Limay, 1907 — P. Ratouis de Limay, A. T. Desfriches, Paris, 1907.

Réau, 1928	L. Réau, 'Watteau 1684–1721' in L. Dimier, *Les Peintres français du* XVIIIè, Paris-Bruxelles, i, 1928, pp. 1–59.
Réau, 1927	L. Réau, 'Hubert Robert, peintre de Paris', *Bulletin de la Société de l'Histoire de l'Art français*, 1927, pp. 207–27.
Reiset, 1869	*Notice des Dessins, Cartons, Pastels, Miniatures et Emeaux exposés dans les Salles du 1er et 2è étage du Musée Impérial du Louvre. Deuxième partie: Ecole Française*, par F. Reiset, Paris, 1869.
Riotor, 1930	L. Riotor, *L'oeuvre décorative, peinte et gravée de J. Pillement*, 1930.
Robert-Jones, 1963	Ph. Robert-Jones, 'Le legs Fernand Honget', *Bulletin des Musées Royaux des Beaux-Arts de Belgique*, 1963, pp. 22–6.
Rosenberg, 1970	P. Rosenberg, 'Twenty French Drawings in Sacramento', *Master Drawings*, 8, 1970, pp. 31–9.
Rosenberg, 1971	P. Rosenberg, *Il Seicento francese*, Milan, 1971.
Rosenberg, Reynaud, Compin, 1974	*Musée du Louvre. Catalogue illustré des Peintures. Ecole française* XVIIè *et* XVIIIè *siècles*, by P. Rosenberg, N. Reynaud et I. Compin, Paris, 1974.
Rouchés-Huyghe	G. R. Rouchés and R. Huyghe, *Cabinet des Dessins du Musée du Louvre. Catalogue raisonné. Ecole française (de J. F. Millet à Ch. Muller)*, Paris, 1938.
Schneider, 1932	H. Schneider, *Jan Lievens, seine Leben und seine Werke*, Haarlem, 1932.
Schneider and Ekkart, 1973	H. Schneider and R. E. O. Ekkart, *Jan Lievens, sein Leben und seine Werke*, Amsterdam, 1973
Sentenac, 1929	P. Sentenac, *Hubert Robert*, Paris, 1929.
Sérullaz-Calvet, 1965	A. Sérullaz-Calvet, 'Un Album de Croquis inédits de Jacques-Louis David', *Revue de l'Art*, no. 5, 1965, pp. 65–8.
Slatkin, 1971	R. Shoolman-Slatkin, 'Two early drawings by François Boucher', *Master Drawings*, IX, 1971, pp. 398 ff.
Slatkin, 1976	R. Shoolman-Slatkin, 'Abraham Blomaert and François Boucher: Affinity and Relationship', *Master Drawings*, 14, 1976, no. 3, pp. 247 ff.
Sterling, Adhémar	Ch. Sterling et H. Adhémar, *Musée National du Louvre. Peintures de l'Ecole française du* XIXè *siècle*, Paris, 1958–61, 4 vols.
Tauzia, 1888	*Musée National du Louvre. Dessins, Cartons, Pastels et Miniatures des diverses Ecoles, exposés depuis 1879 dans les salles du 1er étage. Deuxième notice supplémentaire*, par le Vicomte Both de Tauzia, Paris, 1888.
Tietze, 1944	H. Tietze et E. Tietze-Conrat, *The Drawings of the Venetian Painters in the 15th and 16th Centuries*, New York, 1944.
Vallery-Radot, 1953	J. Vallery-Radot, *Le dessin français au* XVIIè *siècle*, Lausanne, 1953.
Venturi, 1941	L. Venturi, 'Pierre Henri de Valenciennes', *The Art Quarterly*, iv (1941).
Vergnet-Ruiz, 1930	J. Vergnet-Ruiz, 'Oudry, 1686–1755', dans L. Dimier: *Les Peintres français du* XVIIIè *siècle*, II, Paris-Bruxelles, 1930.
Vichot, 1971	J. Vichot, *L'oeuvre des Ozanne. Essai d'inventaire illustré*, Paris, 1971.
Vloberg, 1930	Maurice Vloberg, *Jean Houel, peintre et graveur, 1735–1813*, Paris, 1930.
Waddesdon Manor cat., 1975	*The James A. de Rothschild Collection at Waddesdon Manor. Gold Boxes and Miniatures of the Eighteenth Century*, Fribourg, 1975.
White, 1975	Christopher White, 'A Rembrandt copy after a Titian landscape', *Master Drawings*, 13, 1975, no. 4, pp. 375 ff.
Wildenstein, 1923	Georges Wildenstein. *Un peintre de paysage au* XVIIIè *siècle: Louis Moreau*, Paris, 1923.
Wilhelm, 1948	*Bergeret de Grancourt. Voyage d'Italie 1773–1774*, Introduction et notes de J. Wilhelm, Paris, 1948.
Wollin, 1939	N. G. Wollin, *Desprez en Suède*, Stockholm, 1939.
Wunder, 1968	R. Wunder, 'Charles Michel-Ange Challe', *Apollo*, LXXXVII (1968), pp. 22 ff.

PIERRE PATEL

(Picardy c. 1605 – Paris 1676)

Patel's working life was spent entirely in Paris, where he became a Master in the Guild of Painters in 1635. The principal influence on his style was Simon Vouet. He specialized in landscape and was known as 'the French Claude Lorrain' (Claude, born in the duchy of Lorraine, which was not then a part of France, went as a boy to Rome where he remained for the rest of his life: in the seventeenth century he was not regarded as a French artist). Having assisted Vouet with his tapestry cartoons, Patel collaborated with Eustache Le Sueur in the decoration of the Cabinet de l'Amour in the Hôtel Lambert, and was commissioned to paint a series of landscapes to decorate the apartments of Anne of Austria in the Louvre. In 1656 he was appointed Painter in Ordinary to the King. Between 1666 and 1676 he collaborated in the designs for the well-known series of Gobelin tapestries, *Les Maisons Royales*. Patel's landscapes, which show the influence not only of Claude but also of Laurent La Hyre, are in the classical tradition with buildings and figures: 'he was a master of perspective' wrote Mariette 'and this led him to introduce architectural features into almost all his compositions. He was also skilled at rendering water and this too he used often to include. His only fault was his over-idealized and monotonous way of representing foliage' (*Abecedario*, iv, pp. 88 ff.). He married in 1632 and had two sons, both painters, Jacques, who died young in 1662, and Pierre-Antoine (1648–1707), his pupil and follower, who continued to work in his father's style.

1 LANDSCAPE WITH RUINS

* Black chalk, with touches of white heightening.
270 × 406 mm
Rouen, Musée des Beaux-Arts (975-4-669)

Provenance: H. Baderou (presented by Henri and Suzanne Baderou in 1975).

Inscribed in pen on the old mount, lower left: PATEL.

A characteristic example of Patel's formal style of landscape, in which classical ruins are used to define the relation of the planes of the composition and as vertical elements counterbalancing the oblique direction of the tree-trunks. Black chalk, lightly touched with white, is used with the greatest delicacy in the rendering of foliage – in a way close to La Hyre's – the texture of rocks and stones, and the subtle indications of the distant hills. The grey tone of the whole, which evokes the effect of twilight and gives the landscape a poetic quality, is reminiscent of Le Sueur.

The few other known drawings by Patel include: the study in the Rijksmuseum for the painting from the Hôtel Lambert, now in the Louvre (49.511: Rosenberg, 1971, fig. 24), two drawings in the Louvre (32,282, and 32,283: *Dessins français du* XVIIè *siècle*, exh. Paris (Louvre), 1960, nos. 33–4), and one in Sacramento (394: *French Master Drawings of the 17th and 18th centuries in North American Collections*, exh. Toronto etc., 1972–3, no. 106, fig. 48).

2 LANDSCAPE WITH A RUINED TEMPLE

Black chalk, with watercolour and bodycolour.
256 × 409 mm
Paris, Ecole des Beaux-Arts (1396)

Provenance: E. Desperet (Lugt 721: sale, Paris, 1865, 7–13 June, lot 453); bequeathed by A. Armand and P. Valton in 1908.

Literature: Le Paysage français de Poussin à Corot, exh. Paris (Petit Palais) 1925, no. 636; *French Art*, exh. London (Royal Academy) 1932, no. 1026 (no. 619 in commemorative catalogue); *L'Art français des* XVIIè *et* XVIIIè *siècles*, exh. Paris (Ecole des Beaux-Arts) 1933, no. 117; *Franse Landschap*, exh. Amsterdam, 1951, no. 197; Vallery Radot, 1953, pl. 115; *Dessins français du* XVIIè *siècle*, exh. Paris (Louvre) 1960, under no. 33.

Inscribed in pen, lower left: *Patel F.*

In composition, this drawing comes very close to the painting in the Musée des Beaux-Arts at Orléans (*The Splendid Century: French Art, 1600–1715*, exh. U.S.A., 1960–1, no. 88, repr.), and in the handling of the black chalk it seems equal in quality to no. 1 in the present exhibition. On the other hand, the liveliness of the added colour suggests a more advanced phase of stylistic evolution. The possibility cannot be ruled out that this drawing, though in quality fully worthy of the elder Patel, may be a variation on a composition by him, drawn by his son Pierre-Antoine. The younger Patel is best known for his highly finished drawings in gouache (e.g. one in the Metropolitan Museum, 61.170, and two in the Louvre, RF 1958 and 1952).

ISRAEL SILVESTRE

(Nancy 1621 – Paris 1690)

A native of Lorraine, and grandson of the Claude Henriet who was principal painter at the ducal court there, Silvestre came to Paris in 1631 where he was brought up by his uncle, Israel Henriet, painter and draughtsman to Louis XIII. Between 1639 and 1653 he went more than once to Italy, and it was there, in 1639, that he published his first set of engravings. His manner of engraving was derived from his better known fellow countryman Jacques Callot, and also from Stefano della Bella whom he knew well in Paris in 1642. In 1661 he inherited his uncle's collection of the etched plates of both artists. In the same year he took French nationality and two years later became Engraver in Ordinary to the King, in which capacity he engraved the two well-known series of Royal Festivals – the *Plaisirs de l'Isle Enchantée* (1665) and the *Carrousel de 1662* published in collaboration with François Chauveau and G. Rousselet (1670). From 1668 onwards he began the series of engravings of the royal châteaux. He was elected a probationary member of the Académie Royale in 1666 and a full member in 1670. In 1667 he was appointed drawing master to the Royal Pages (his *Leçons données aux pages du Roy par le Sieur Silvestre pour apprendre à dessiner la fortification et le paysage* was published by Jean Mariette) and in 1673 to the Dauphin. He died at the age of seventy in the Louvre, where he had lived since 1668. The full extent of his achievement as a draughtsman is not yet fully appreciated: though the pen drawings that he made for engravings are precise to the point of dryness, his watercolour views drawn on the spot combine topographical accuracy with an unusual freshness of vision and an exact sense of colour that put him on a level with Van der Meulen.

3 THE FORTRESS OF JAMETZ
*
Watercolour over black chalk and pen and brown ink.
392 × 889 mm
Louvre, Cabinet des Dessins (33,058)
Literature: B. Belin, *Dessins d'I. Silvestre au Cabinet des Dessins du Louvre*, (unpublished thesis, Paris 1968), no. 60.

Inscribed by the artist in ink, in the sky to the right of centre: *Jametz* and in the moat, to right of the fortress: *fossé* (and in black chalk) *eaux*.

An engraving of this subject is inscribed: *Veüe du Château de Jametz. Israel Silvestre delin. et sculpsit* (L. E. Faucheux, *Catalogue raisonné de toutes les estampes qui forment l'oeuvre d'Israel Silvestre*, Paris, 1857, p. 234, no 24).

In the autumn of 1665 Silvestre was instructed by Colbert to go to Champagne and Lorraine to draw views of some of the fortresses recently taken by the French. During this and subsequent journeys he produced a series of watercolour drawings remarkable for their freshness of vision. The present drawing comes from an album of such views, formerly in the Royal Collection and now in the Louvre (33,010–33,086).

Jametz was a fortress near Verdun, on the river Loison. The Duke of Lorraine ceded it to Louis XIV, who later gave it to the Prince de Condé.

ADAM FRANS VAN DER MEULEN

(Brussels 1632 – Paris 1690)

Van der Meulen was brought up in the tradition of Rubens by the Antwerp master Pieter Snayers, and soon made a name for himself with 'his skill in representing battles, sieges and other military actions' (Mariette, *Abecedario*, v, p. 364). In 1664 he came to France and entered the service of Louis XIV at the invitation of the King's minister Colbert acting on the advice of Charles Le Brun who had recently been appointed *premier peintre du roi*. His arrival marked the beginning of his close friendship and collaboration with Le Brun, which continued until the death of both artists in the same year, 1690. He was given apartments in the Gobelins tapestry factory, and though the King valued him as a painter (e.g. at Marly, and his part in the decoration of the Escalier des Ambassadeurs at Versailles), his principal work was his often extensive share in some of the great series of tapestries produced there, including *Les Maisons Royales*, the *Four Seasons*, the *History of Louis* XIV and the *Conquests of Louis* XIV. In order to carry out the landscape backgrounds for this last series he accompanied the King on no fewer than nine of his campaigns; the care with which he studied each place is shown by the number of sketches and watercolours which he made on the spot and which Mariette praised 'for the exact rendering of the buildings and the beautiful drawing of the trees; the delicate brushwork and the intelligent use of colour'. Van der Meulen was assisted in these undertakings by a whole school of landscape draughtsmen that he gathered round him, including his fellow-countrymen Abraham Genoels (1640–1723), Adrien Frans Bauduin (1644–1711) and Gerard Scotin (*c.* 1643–1715). The activity of this Flemish colony in Paris was to have a considerable influence on the French landscape of the early eighteenth century.

4 THE OUTSKIRTS OF A FLEMISH TOWN
* Watercolour over black chalk.
285 × 408 mm, continued on the left on an added strip of paper, the left corner cut.
Louvre, Cabinet des Dessins (20,083)

Literature: Lugt: 1949, no. 857, pl. xcix; *Dessins flamands*, exh. Paris (Louvre) 1952, no. 857; *L'Art français et l'Europe aux* XVIIe *et* XVIIIe *siècles*, exh. Paris (Orangerie) 1958, no. 106; *Van der Meulen, peintre des Conquêtes de Louis* XIV, exh. Douai, 1967, no. 21; Rosenberg, 1971, pl. XXIV.

A characteristic example of the kind of drawing that Van der Meulen must have made directly on the spot when accompanying Louis XIV on one of his campaigns. After the artist's death in 1690 his portfolios of sketches became Crown property, and apart from the group of drawings now in the Louvre that were in the King's personal collection the rest of the studies and sketches that he made in connection with his official commissions are still preserved in the Gobelins tapestry factory. They were catalogued in 1902 by Jules Guiffrey (*Inventaire des richesses d'art de la France: Paris, Monuments Civils*, vol. iii) and a large selection of them was exhibited in 1931 (*Van der Meulen*, exh. Paris (Manufacture des Gobelins), 1931; see also *Bulletin de la Société de l'Histoire de l'Art Français*, 1931, pp. 6 ff.)

5 PANORAMIC LANDSCAPE WITH A VILLAGE ON THE EDGE OF A SCARP
Watercolour, over faint underdrawing in black chalk.
100 × 410 mm
Louvre, Cabinet des Dessins (20,088)

Literature: Lugt, 1949, no. 858.

It is instructive to compare this drawing, with its emphasis on topographical accuracy and its scrupulous regard for tonal values, with those of an earlier Flemish painter who also worked in France, Jacques Fouquier (1590–1642). His drawings, with their brilliant colour and exaggerated effects, are strongly influenced by Rubens, with whom he had worked in Antwerp. But the sincerity and restraint of Van der Meulen are not incompatible with a vein of genuine poetry.

FRANÇOIS DESPORTES

(Champigneulles 1661 – Paris 1743)

Desportes, born in Champagne of a peasant family, was little more than a boy when he went to Paris. The Flemish influence in his style comes from his master Nicasius Bernaert, who had been a pupil of Snyders. Like Oudry (q.v.) in the next generation, whose career developed along rather similar lines, Desportes became the leading animal and still-life painter of his day and the recognized official recorder of the activities in the hunting-field of Louis XIV and Louis XV – then regarded as an important part of the ceremonial of the court. He was also celebrated for his portraits, and in 1699 was elected to the Académie Royale on the strength of a self-portrait in hunting costume (now in the Louvre). He worked for Louis XIV, for whom he painted decorations in the Ménagerie at Versailles and the châteaux at Marly, Choisy, Compiègne and Chantilly, and also made cartoons for the Gobelins factory, including those for one of its most important series of tapestries, *Les Nouvelles Indes* (1737–40). He had many other patrons, French and foreign; in 1695–6 he was working for the King of Poland and in 1712 he made a brief visit to England.

Desportes differs from Oudry in that in his finished work landscape is always a subsidiary element – either a background for portraits and hunting-scenes or a naturalistic setting for animal-paintings; but his feeling for it is evident even in this restricted form, and even more evident in his oil-sketches, twelve of which are here exhibited. These come from a very large collection of studies in oil on paper, not only of landscape but also of animals, flowers and plants and even pieces of silverware, which were part of the working-material of his studio, and which he constantly referred to for ideas and pictorial motifs. They were preserved *en bloc* by his family until 1784, when about six-hundred were purchased for the Sèvres manufactory as a source of inspiration for the decorators of the porcelain (see Hourticq, 1920, pp. 117 ff.; Lechevallier-Chevignard, 1920, pp. 164 ff.; Quignon, 1920, pp. 353 ff.; M. Brunet, preface to *Paysages de F. Desportes*, exh. cat. Compiègne, 1961). At some time in the present century, some of them were deposited in other museums: at Compiègne; the Musée de la Chasse et de la Nature in Paris; the Musée de la Chasse à Tir at Gien. An isolated example, not a landscape, is the beautiful sheet with two sketches of a kitten, in the Fitzwilliam Museum, Cambridge, which when acquired was believed to be by Oudry.

Desportes's son, Claude-François (1695–1774) described how his father used to go hunting with Louis XIV, carrying with him a little sketchbook in which he made rapid notes of the actions and movements of animals; 'and he did the same with landscape; he used to take with him into the country tin boxes containing his brushes and palette ready prepared, and also a walking stick with on one end a steel spike that could be driven into the ground and on the other a steel knob which opened to allow a little easel, also made of steel, to be screwed in, which served to support his drawing-paper' (Address to the Académie in 1748).

Desportes's practice of sketching in oil marks the beginning of the tradition among French landscape-painters which was continued later in the eighteenth century by Joseph Vernet (q.v.) and P.-H. de Valenciennes (q.v.) and at the beginning of the nineteenth by Corot and his circle in Rome (though since Desportes's sketches remained in the possession of his descendants until 1784 they can have had little direct influence). These artists, whose finished work was of a formal character, made oil-sketches as exercises and memoranda for their own use.

6 A RIVER VALLEY

Oil on paper mounted on panel.
208 × 495 mm
Compiègne, Musée National (Pp 4, 1814, no. 13, S.24)
Literature: *Oeuvres de Desportes*, exh. Beauvais, 1920–1,
no. 71; *Landscape in French Art, 1550–1900*, exh.
London (Royal Academy) 1949, no. 130; *Paysages de F.
Desportes*, exh. Compiègne, 1961, no. 48, pl. 5.

7 VIEW ACROSS A VALLEY WITH A FORMAL GARDEN AND
* POOL IN THE FOREGROUND

Oil on paper mounted on panel.
300 × 530 mm
Compiègne, Musée National (Pp 2, 1814, no. 76, S.15)
Literature: *Oeuvres de Desportes*, exh. Beauvais, 1920–1,
no. 48; *Paysages de F. Desportes*, exh. Compiègne, 1961,
no. 40, pl. 2.

8 A WOOD BEHIND A PARK WALL

Oil on paper mounted on canvas.
290 × 480 mm
Compiègne, Musée National (Pp 4, 1814, no. 21, S.18)
Literature: *Oeuvres de Desportes*, exh. Beauvais, 1920–1,
no. 116; *Paysages de F. Desportes*, exh. Compiègne,
1961, no. 42, pl. 12.

9 A FIELD BORDERED BY TREES, WITH COWS GRAZING AND
* PINE-TREES IN THE FOREGROUND

Oil on paper mounted on panel.
210 × 510 mm
Compiègne, Musée National (Pp 2, 1814, no. 76, S.15)
Literature: *Oeuvres de Desportes*, Beauvais, 1920–1, no.
144; *Le Paysage français de Poussin à Corot*, exh. Paris,
1925, no. 729; *Paysages de F. Desportes*, exh.
Compiègne, 1961, no. 39, pl. 11.
Inscribed in pen, in the same hand, top and bottom:
N^{ro}4.

10 A SLOPING FIELD WITH A WOOD BEYOND

Oil on paper mounted on cardboard.
190 × 520 mm
Sèvres, Manufacture Nationale de Porcelaines (Pp 4,
1814, no. 8, V.11)
Literature: *Paysages de F. Desportes*, exh. Compiègne,
1961, no. 10.
Inscribed in ink near the top edge: N^{ro} *10*, and in top
right corner: *10*.

11 A POND AT THE FOOT OF A CLIFF

Oil on paper mounted on cardboard.
260 × 485 mm
Sèvres, Manufacture Nationale de Porcelaines (P 2,
1814, no. 95, V.18)

Literature: *Paysages de F. Desportes*, exh. Compiègne,
1961, no. 17.

12 A BANK WITH TREES BEYOND AND PLANTS IN THE
* FOREGROUND

Oil on paper mounted on cardboard.
295 × 500 mm
Sèvres, Manufacture Nationale de Porcelaines (P 2,
1814, no. 100, V.26)
Literature: *Paysages de F. Desportes*, exh. Compiègne,
1961, no. 25.

13 CLOSE-UP VIEW OF A MOSSY BANK WITH PLANTS AND
GRASSES

Oil on paper mounted on cardboard.
305 × 510 mm
Sèvres, Manufacture Nationale de Porcelaines (P 2,
1814, no. 97, V, 29)
Literature: *Paysages de F. Desportes*, exh. Compiègne,
1961, no. 28, pl. 3.
Inscribed in pen, lower left corner: N^{ro} . . . (the figure
has been trimmed away).

In this sketch are combined the artist's sense of
composition with the scientific accuracy of the
botanist. Desportes's chief patron, Louis XIV,
appreciated his concern for truth to nature: 'the late
king recognized with pleasure in Desportes's works
the places that he had come to know well when out
hunting. M. Fagon, his chief physician, who was also a
skilled botanist, enjoyed explaining to him the names
of all the plants represented, even down to the little
flowers and herbs which decorated the garden terraces'
(Claude-François Desportes, Address to the Académie
de Peinture, 1748: Dussieux, Soulié, Chennevières,
1854, ii, p. 110).

14 ROSE-BUSHES

Oil on paper mounted on cardboard.
305 × 505 mm
Sèvres, Manufacture Nationale de Porcelaines (F 7,
1814, no. 208, III, 31)

15 BURDOCKS

Oil on paper mounted on cardboard.
290 × 505 mm
Sèvres, Manufacture Nationale de Porcelaines (F 7,
1814, no. 1: III, 20)
Literature: *Paysages de F. Desportes*, exh. Compiègne,
1961, no. 32.
Inscribed in pen, top centre: N^{ro}*27* (crossed out).

16 A BED OF WORM-EATEN CABBAGES

* Oil on paper mounted on cardboard.
365 × 530 mm
Sèvres, Manufacture Nationale de Porcelaines (Fp 3, 1814, no. 30: S.242)

17 SIX TREE-STUMPS

Oil on paper mounted on cardboard.
265 × 460 mm
Sèvres, Manufacture Nationale de Porcelaines (F 7, 1814, no. 5: III, 46)

Literature: Paysages de F. Desportes, exh. Compiègne, 1961, no. 35.

Inscribed lower centre, with the sheet upside down, in pen: *N.ro 15.*

CLAUDE GILLOT

(Langres 1673 – Paris 1722)

Gillot developed along highly individual lines, unaffected by the example of his master, J.-B. Corneille. The dominant influence reflected in his paintings, and even more obviously in his drawings and etchings, was his interest in the world of the theatre, especially the Comédie Italienne. For most of his working life the Comédie itself was banished from France (the troupe was expelled in 1697 and did not return until 1716) but its repertoire was taken over by the marionette theatres and companies of strolling players which performed at the great Parisian fairs of St Germain (cf. no. 61) and St Laurent. It was these performances that inspired Gillot's famous series of drawings of the Comédie Italienne, executed in a lively style in a combination of pen and ink and red wash. Most of them were etched, either by himself or by Huquier (Populus, 1930, nos. 17–20 and 342–53). He also designed the costumes for two productions of operas by Lully, *Amadis* and *Thesée*, and for the *Ballet des Eléments* (1721).

Though Gillot is now chiefly remembered as the originator of the early eighteenth-century vogue for theatrical subjects (and especially for influencing in this direction his pupil, Watteau, q.v.), the combination of landscape with imaginary figures that he evolved was one of the forerunners of the *fête galante*, which was to become one of the most significant manifestations of landscape in France.

18 A DRUMMER IN A LANDSCAPE, WITH A COLUMN OF SOLDIERS IN THE BACKGROUND

Pen and brown ink.
160 × 204 mm
Louvre, Cabinet des Dessins (26,770)

Literature: Guiffrey-Marcel, vi, no. 4221, repr.

Inscribed in pen, lower left: *original de M.Gillot*, and numbered top right: *I*.

The same inscription, in the same hand, occurs on three other drawings in the Louvre, of much the same size as the present drawing and likewise numbered in Roman figures from II to IV. In each of them the landscape, freely sketched in pen in a way that almost suggests etching, is the setting for one or more figures: a woman and child with a soldier in no. II (26,773: Guiffrey-Marcel, no. 422, repr.); a shepherd and shepherdess in no. III (26,774; Guiffrey-Marcel, no. 4223, repr.); a shepherdess and a drummer in no. IV (26,771; Guiffrey-Marcel, no. 4224, repr.). It seems not to have been observed that the type of the figures and their relation to the landscape setting in compositions of this type by Gillot foreshadow Watteau's development of the *fête galante*.

ANTOINE WATTEAU

(*Valenciennes 1684 – Nogent-sur-Marne 1721*)

Watteau stands out as the leading personality in the French art of the first half of the eighteenth century. At the beginning of that period, when the artistic world was divided between the followers of Rubens and the followers of Poussin, it was the combination of Flemish and Venetian elements in his work that eventually reconciled these opposing factions; and the entirely new kind of sensibility that he developed, both in his choice of subjects and in his treatment of them, exercised a decisive influence on French taste in the period before the emergence of Neo-Classicism.

After a short time in the studio of J. A. Gérin in Valenciennes, Watteau came to Paris in 1702. There he studied under Claude Gillot (q.v.), from whom he acquired his mastery of the technique of drawing and also his intimate familiarity with the world of the Comédie Italienne. His collaboration in 1708–9 over various decorative projects with Claude Audran III brought him the revelation – of fundamental importance for his development – of Rubens's *Marie de Médicis* cycle (Louvre), then housed in the Palais du Luxembourg of which Audran was custodian. In 1712 he was elected an associate (*agréé*) member of the Académie Royale de Peinture, and in 1717 a full member, as a painter of *fêtes galantes*, on the strength of his painting *L'Embarquement pour Cythère* (Louvre: later version in Charlottenburg Museum, Berlin). At about this time he became a friend of the great patron and collector Pierre Crozat, who commissioned the series of *The Four Seasons* and encouraged him to study his unrivalled collection of drawings by the Old Masters (see no. 19). In 1719 he paid a brief visit to London, where he received several commissions which were eventually executed by his associate and follower Philippe Mercier. After his return to Paris he produced one of his greatest masterpieces, the shop-sign for his friend the picture-dealer Gersaint (Charlottenburg Museum, Berlin), but in the next year he died of consumption at the age of thirty-seven. After his death, his friend Jean de Jullienne published a series of facsimile engravings of his drawings under the title *Figures de différents caractères de paysages et d'études dessinées d'après nature*. Though few of his landscape studies seem in fact to have been made directly from nature, the role of the outdoor settings in his *fêtes galantes* and the influence on his landscape style of the masters of the sixteenth century, especially the Titian-Campagnola circle in Venice, were to play a fundamental part in the later development of French landscape.

19 TWO FIGURES IN A LANDSCAPE (AFTER DOMENICO CAMPAGNOLA)

Red chalk. The ruled border in pen and brown ink.
233 × 232 mm
Louvre, Cabinet des Dessins (33,374)

Provenance: P.-J. Mariette (Lugt 1852; sale, Paris, 1775, part of lot 779).

Literature: Reiset, 1869, no. 1342; Borenius, 1924, p. 279, repr.; Réau, 1928, p. 7; Dacier, 1930, no. 35, repr.; *Künstlerkopien*, exh. Basle, 1937, no. 8, p. 66; Parker-Mathey, 1957, i, no. 438, repr.; *Le cabinet d'un grand amateur, P.-J. Mariette*, exh. Paris (Louvre), 1967, 279; Cormack, 1970, p. 25, pls. 31, 129.

In the catalogue which he drew up for the sale of the collection of Quentin de Lorangère in 1774, the picture-dealer and *expert* Edmond-François Gersaint referred to Watteau's 'interest in the Old Masters, whom he took as his models and whose works he used carefully to copy whenever the opportunity offered'. When Watteau was invited by the great collector Pierre Crozat to decorate a room in his house in the rue Richelieu he accepted the commission 'all the more willingly because of the opportunity this would give him of making fresh discoveries among the drawings and paintings by the Old Masters of which the house was full' (Mariette, *Abecedario*, vi, p. 105). Of the drawings, Watteau was particularly interested in the sixteenth-century Venetian landscapes. As the comte de Caylus wrote 'he was enchanted, in the drawings by Titian and Campagnola that he saw – or, one might more truly say, discovered – there, by the beauty of the scenery and the buildings in them, and by the rendering of the foliage' (Fontaine, 1910, p. 15). The originals of the two copies of such drawings that are here exhibited were probably in Crozat's collection.

The original drawing by Campagnola is now in the Albertina (24,364). Like the copy, it bears the collector's mark of P.-J. Mariette. The two formed part of lot 779 in his sale in 1775, as is established by the thumb-nail sketches made by Gabriel de Saint-Aubin in the margins of his copy of the catalogue, now in the Museum of Fine Arts in Boston: 'five other landscapes [by Titian] together with copies in red chalk of two of them drawn with great liveliness by Ant. Watteau'. The attribution of the original drawing to Titian was followed by W. G. Constable (*Burlington Magazine*, xlii (1923), p. 192), the Tietzes (1944, no. 1970), D. von Hadeln (1924, no. 7) and R. Pallucchini (1969, p. 330). More recently, however, it has been given by K. Oberhuber to Domenico Campagnola (Koschatsky, Oberhuber, Knab, no. 61, repr.; *Dessins italiens de l'Albertina*, exh. Paris (Louvre), 1975, no. 53, repr.; *Disegni di Tiziano e della sua cerchia*, exh. Venice (Fondazione Cini), 1976, no. 67, repr.).

The original – like almost all landscape drawings of the Titian-Campagnola type – is in pen and brown ink, but Watteau's copies are in red chalk. In spite of this difference in technique and the characteristic facial types and treatment of the hands, the copy is a remarkably faithful one. In some ways it has even improved on the original: the relation of the planes of the composition have been clarified and the pose of the right-hand figure is better understood.

The Venetian drawings that Watteau copied were not only in the Crozat Collection. He also had access to the Cabinet du Roi, of which his friend Antoine Coypel was curator. There is in the Louvre a landscape drawing by Domenico Campagnola (5550), acquired by Louis xiv in 1671 as part of the Jabach Collection, and also a superb copy in red chalk (5577), confiscated during the Revolution from the Saint-Morys Collection (see p. 90), which M. Jaffé has convincingly attributed to the hand of Watteau.

20   LANDSCAPE WITH A BEAR ATTACKING A GOAT (AFTER TITIAN?)

Red chalk.
210 × 300 mm
Paris, Institut Néerlandais, Fondation Custodia (3803)

Provenance: G. Bourgarel (sale, Paris, 15–16 June 1922, lot 74); E. Rodrigues (Lugt 899; sale, Paris, 28 November 1928, lot 242, pl. 38, bt. F. Lugt); F. Lugt (Lugt 1028).

Literature: Parker, 1931, pp. 25 and 43, pl. 15; *Watteau*

als Teckenaar, exh. Amsterdam, 1935, no. 45; Parker-Mathey, 1957, i, no. 437; *Le Dessin français dans les collections hollandaises*, exh. Paris-Amsterdam, 1964, no. 35, pl. 45; *Watteau et sa génération*, exh. Paris (Galerie Cailleux), 1968, no. 17; White, 1975, pp. 375 ff., fig. 1; Muraro-Rosand, 1976, p. 100, note 9; *Hommage à Titien*, exh. Paris (Institut Néerlandais), no. 19, pl. 16.

A copy by Watteau of a Venetian landscape drawing which he probably knew when in the Crozat Collection (see no. 19). The original, which has disappeared, may well have been by Titian himself (see *Hommage à Titien*, pp. 31 f.). Three other copies are known, all in pen and brown ink. One, likewise in the Fondation Custodia (6584), was for a long time believed to be Titian's original (*Le dessin italien dans les collections hollandaises*, exh. Paris-Rotterdam-Haarlem, 1962, no. 75, pl. liv) but has now been identified, independently, by J. Byam Shaw and C. White as a copy by Rembrandt (White, 1975, pp. 375 ff., pl. 23; *Hommage à Titien*, no. 18, pl. 17). The others both lack the group of the bear and the goat: one, now in the Louvre (8084: White, 1975, p. 377, fig. 2), was acquired by the Cabinet du Roi in 1671 as part of the Jabach Collection; the other, by the diarist John Evelyn, signed and dated *J. Evelyn Imitavit 1656*, was sold at Christie's on 14 June 1977 (lot 154).

Watteau's practice of making copies of landscape drawings by sixteenth-century Venetian masters not only enabled him to study their methods, but provided him, as did his sheets of studies of separate figures and heads, with a source of pictorial motifs. M. P. Eidelberg (1967, pp. 173 ff.) has pointed out that one such copy, in the Art Institute of Chicago (Parker-Mathey, i, no. 427), was used for the background of the painting *La Leçon d'amour* in the Nationalmuseum, Stockholm. Watteau's activity as a landscape draughtsman was not confined to copying and reinterpreting the work of his predecessors. Though many of his landscape drawings have now disappeared – of the twelve engraved in the publication *Figures de différents caractères*, only one is now known (Parker-Mathey, i, no. 457) – contemporary evidence and some of the drawings that have survived establish that he also drew directly from nature, sometimes in Paris in the Luxembourg Gardens or the Faubourg des Porcherons, or in Crozat's garden at Montmorency, or, in the last months of his life, at Nogent-sur-Marne. Lot 1392 at the Mariette Sale of 1775 consisted of 'four views of the country round Paris, in red chalk' by Watteau.

21   THE FINDING OF MOSES
*

Red chalk.
215 × 303 mm
Paris, Ecole des Beaux-Arts (D. 1604)

Provenance: J. Boilly (sale, Paris, 19 March 1869, lot 225); A. Armand and P. Valton, by whom bequeathed in 1908.

Literature: Lavallée, 1928, p. 10, no. 5, repr.; Dacier, 1930, no. 44, repr.; Parker, 1931, pp. 25 and 43, pl. 24; *French Art*, exh. London (Royal Academy), 1932, no. 774 (Commemorative Catalogue, no. 785, pl. clxv); *Chefs d'oeuvre de l'art français*, exh. Paris, 1937, no. 587; Lavallée, 1948, p. 68; *Landscape in French Art*, exh. London (Royal Academy), 1949, no. 436; *Het Franse Landschap*, exh. Amsterdam, 1951, no. 225, pl. 35; Boucher and Jaccottet, 1952, no. 13, repr.; Parker and Mathey, 1957, ii, no. 859; Bacou, 1970, pl. vii.

A rare example of a study for a complete composition, characteristic of Watteau both in the scale of the figures and the skill with which they and the landscape setting are integrated; but this typical park of the Ile de France is the setting not for the usual *fête galante* but for a scene from the Old Testament. The unusual choice of subject and the large scale and evident importance of the composition – evident even in this rapid sketch – have prompted the suggestion that Watteau may at some stage have intended this subject for the *morceau de réception* which he was obliged to offer to the Académie Royale on his election in 1717, and which in the event was the Louvre version of the *Embarquement pour Cythère*.

His treatment of the main group in the right foreground, of Pharaoh's daughter and her attendants, one of whom is kneeling with the infant Moses in her arms, is clearly inspired by Paolo Veronese's painting, now in Washington but then in the Crozat Collection, which is an enlarged autograph version of one in the Prado (G. Piovene and R. Marini, *L'opera completa del Veronese*, Milan, 1968, pl. liii). Watteau made copies of at least two details from it (Parker-Mathey, i, nos. 345, 352).

The same painting inspired a red chalk drawing of the subject by Watteau's friend Charles de La Fosse (Besançon, Musée des Beaux-Arts, D. 2722: Lavallée, 1948, pl. xxviii), also a member of Crozat's circle.

JEAN-BAPTISTE OUDRY

(Paris 1686 – Beauvais 1755)

Oudry began his career as a portrait-painter and then, like Desportes whose tradition he continued, turned to animals and still-life. He later became the recognised official painter of the activities of the royal hunt. The best-known series of these hunting scenes was made for the Gobelins tapestry factory, of which he was put in charge in 1736, having two years before been appointed Director of the factory at Beauvais. From the very beginning of his career, landscape played a major part in his work, and his remarkable talent for it is particularly apparent in his drawings. He developed independently of any Italian influence, under the inspiration of the Dutch and Flemish masters whom he had studied as a pupil in the studio of Nicolas de Largillière and by direct observation of the French countryside in the neighbourhood of Paris and Beauvais. The centre of his activity and of his influence as a draughtsman was the Prince de Guise's park at Arcueil, to which he had the privilege of entry (see no. 27) and where younger artists such as Portail, Natoire, Boucher and Pierre Wille came to profit from his instruction and follow his example by sketching in the park and gardens.

– FOUR VIEWS FROM AN ALBUM OF LANDSCAPE-DRAWINGS
Pen and brown ink and wash, heightened with white, on blue paper.

Provenance: Comte de l'Espine; his daughter, Princess de Croÿ, by whom presented to the Louvre in 1930.

These four sheets were part of an album (now broken up) which contained twenty-seven drawings representing various types of landscape, all without figures. The inscription on the frontispiece of the album gives the date when it was begun: '*Livre de dessein d'après nature et de geny commencé au mois de Juin 1714 par Jan Oudry*'. These are the earliest known landscape drawings by the artist and show the influence of the Dutch and Flemish landscape-painters whom he had studied in Largillière's studio. They were no doubt used as a source of decorative motifs, for similar details often occur in the backgrounds of his paintings and tapestries. As the artist himself states in the inscription quoted above, they are partly imaginary and partly based on direct observation.

2 A WALLED ENCLOSURE AND HOUSES AMONG TREES ON THE EDGE OF A HILL
198 × 255 mm
Louvre. Cabinet des Dessins (RF 14,957)
Literature: Opperman, 1972, ii, 2, p. 814, cat. D. 1041; Duclaux, 1975, no. 271, repr. p. 149.

3 A LAKE AMONG ROCKY HILLS
200 × 257 mm
Louvre. Cabinet des Dessins (RF 14,958)
Literature: Opperman, 1972, ii, 2, p. 814, cat. D. 1042; Duclaux, 1975, no. 272, repr. p. 149.

24 A HOUSE AND TREES BESIDE A RIVER
203 × 254 mm
Louvre. Cabinet des Dessins (RF 14,963)
Literature: Opperman, 1972, ii, 2, p. 815, cat. D. 1047; Duclaux, 1975, no. 277, repr. p. 151.

25 A STREAM WITH A SLUICE
198 × 255 mm
Louvre. Cabinet des Dessins (RF 14,964)
Literature: Opperman, 1972, ii, 2, p. 815, cat. D. 1048, fig. 28; Duclaux, 1975, no. 278, repr. p. 151.

26 THE WOLF HUNT: THE KILL
*
Pen and brown and black ink and grey and brown wash over black chalk, heightened with white, on blue (faded to greenish-blue) paper.
386 × 527 mm
Louvre. Cabinet des Dessins (31,493)
Provenance: Revolutionary confiscation

Literature: Locquin, 1912, no. 663; Vergnet-Ruiz, 1930, cat. ii. p. 175, no. 14; *Dessins du xviiième siecle*, exh. Paris (Louvre), 1967, no. 23, pl. iii; Opperman, 1972, ii, 2, cat. 578, fig. 189; Duclaux, 1975, no. 232, repr. p.141.

Signed and dated in ink, lower left: *J. B. Oudry 1728*.

The treatment of the forest background marks a definite stage in Oudry's evolution as a landscape artist. The date inscribed on the drawing shows that it belongs to the same period as the series of royal commissions for paintings and tapestries of hunting subjects, between the *Chasses Nouvelles* of 1727 and the better known *Chasses Royales* begun in 1733

(Opperman, 1970, pp. 217 ff.). The elaborate technique recalls that of the drawings in the 1714 album (see nos. 22–5); but the landscape, though still a subsidiary and decorative element, is freely treated and has become an important part of the composition. Oudry's later, realistic, approach to nature is foreshadowed in his careful rendering of the trunks and foliage of the trees and the effect of light through the leaves.

27 A FLIGHT OF STEPS AMONG TREES IN THE PARK AT
* ARCUEIL

Black chalk heightened with white bodycolour on faded (greenish-blue) blue paper.
325 × 472 mm
Louvre, Cabinet des Dessins (31,491)

Provenance: P.-J. Mariette (Lugt 1852: sale, Paris 1775, part of lot 1306, purchased for the Cabinet du Roi).

Literature: Reiset, 1869, no. 1214; Locquin, 1912, no. 861; Vergnet-Ruiz, 1930, cat. ii, p. 181, no. 138; Desguines, 1950, pp. 8 and 12, pl. A 4; Opperman, 1972, ii. 2, cat. D. 1051; Duclaux, 1975, no. 281, repr.

Signed in pen, lower left: *Oudry à Arcueil* and dated (in another ink) *1744*.

The park and gardens of the Prince de Guise at Arcueil, a few miles south of Paris on the little river Bièvre, were allowed finally to fall into disuse in 1752 and have long ago disappeared. Oudry discovered the place in about 1742 and it soon became a favourite haunt; he found particularly congenial the contrast of nature running wild within an ordered setting. Arcueil inspired several of his paintings, chief of which is the *Wooded landscape with the Aqueduct of Arcueil* painted in 1745 and now in the Museum at Schwerin (Opperman, 1972, ii, 1, cat. P. 608, fig. 309); but the most important result of his habit of visiting these picturesquely neglected gardens was the well-known series of drawings of which the present drawing and no. 28 form part. Executed mainly in the years between 1742 and 1747, when he was at the height of his powers, they reveal his technical mastery and the originality of his approach to landscape: a searching realism allied to a sensitive feeling for the play of reflected lights and shadows, rendered with unique skill by the simple combination of black chalk and white bodycolour on blue paper. Though Oudry was not the only artist to make drawings at Arcueil, he evidently felt a particular affinity with the place, which was for him what the Villa d'Este at Tivoli was to be for Fragonard and Hubert Robert in the 1760's. His views of Arcueil are justly the most celebrated, and have been sought after by collectors from the eighteenth century onwards. The four in the Louvre (Duclaux, 1975, nos. 281–4) belonged to the great collector of Oudry's period, P.-J. Mariette. Others are in the Ecole des Beaux-Arts (including no. 28 in the present exhibition), the Musée de l'Ile de France at Sceaux, the Musée Carnavalet (*Dessins Parisiens*, 1971, no. 89), the Fitzwilliam

Museum in Cambridge (*Dessins Français*, exh. Paris, [Galerie Heim] 1976, no. 75, repr.), the Berlin Printroom, the Courtauld Institute in London, the Metropolitan Museum in New York, the Staatliche Museum in Schwerin and the Albertina in Vienna.

In most of Oudry's drawings of Arcueil the effect of romantic solitude is heightened by the absence of figures, but in the early nineteenth century some of them passed through the hands of a dealer who sought to enliven them by adding figures in the costume of his own period (see E. de Goncourt, *La Maison d'un artiste*, 1881, i, p. 130). The figures in no. 27, however, are by Oudry himself: not only are they in the costume of his day, but the drawing passed directly from Mariette's sale in 1775 to the Cabinet du Roi, and thence to the Louvre.

28 A TRELLIS-WORK SCREEN AND PERGOLA IN THE PARK AT
* ARCUEIL

Black chalk, heightened with white, on blue paper.
305 × 525 mm
Paris, Ecole des Beaux-Arts (1380)
Provenance: A. Armand; P. Valton Bequest.

Literature: Locquin, 1912, no. 873; Vergnet-Ruiz, 1930, cat. ii, p. 181, no. 146; *L'Art des jardins*, exh. Rotterdam, 1948, no. 173; Desguines, 1950, p. 8, repr. p. 33, pl. A VI; *L'Art français du XVIIIe siècle*, exh. Paris (Ecole des Beaux-Arts), 1965, no. 69; Opperman, 1972, ii, 2, cat. D. 1072.

See no. 27.

29 WASHERWOMEN BY A BRIDGE

Brown wash over pencil.
306 × 450 mm
Louvre, Cabinet des Dessins (31,492)

Provenance: Revolutionary confiscation.

Literature: Locquin, 1912, no. 863; Vergnet-Ruiz, 1930, ii, p. 181, no. 141, pl. 34; Opperman, 1972, ii, 2, cat. D. 1105, fig. 368; Duclaux, 1975, no. 285, repr.

Signed and dated in pen, lower left: *J. B. Oudry 1750*.

In style and technique this drawing differs from Oudry's views of Arcueil, which were drawn directly from nature. It is closer to his preparatory studies for paintings of about the same period: compare particularly the drawing, also dated 1750, in the Kunsthaus in Zurich (1944. 12; Opperman, 1972, ii, 2, cat. D. 1103, fig. 364) which is connected with the painting *The farm* in the Louvre (7044; cat. 1974, ii, no. 609, repr. p. 28).

Oudry always urged his pupils to study Dutch seventeenth-century landscape. Both the composition and the feeling of this drawing show that until the very end of his life he remained responsive to this influence, especially to that of Nicholas Berchem. There is in the Louvre a copy by Oudry, also dated 1750 (Duclaux, 1975, no. 287, repr. p. 157), of a drawing by Berchem also in the Louvre.

PIERRE-JEAN MARIETTE
(Paris 1694 – Paris 1774)

Mariette is chiefly remembered for his collection of drawings, one of the finest ever brought together by a single individual. His father, Jean Mariette, was well known as an engraver and publisher at the sign of the *Colonnes d'Hercule* in the rue St Jacques. In 1717 the younger Mariette, though only in his early twenties, was sent for to Vienna to classify and put in order Prince Eugène of Savoy's collection of prints. Having returned home by way of Venice, where he came to know Rosalba Carriera and A. M. Zanetti, he became one of the intimate circle of the collector Pierre Crozat, and was commissioned to compile the catalogue of his collection of drawings for the sale held after his death in 1741. Mariette's father died in the following year and in 1750 he gave up print-dealing in order to devote himself to studying the lives and works of artists (a selection of his notes was published between 1851 and 1860 by Philippe de Chennevières and A. de Montaiglon under the title *Abecedario*) and to the formation of his own collection, the posthumous dispersal of which in 1775 was a landmark in the artistic life of Paris in the second half of the century. The thirteen hundred drawings acquired for the Royal Collection at the sale include some of the finest in the Louvre.

Mariette's fame as a connoisseur and collector has eclipsed his modest but genuine achievement as an original draughtsman. The drawing exhibited here illustrates the interest in landscape felt by the amateur draughtsmen of the period, and also this particular draughtsman's taste for the Bolognese landscape of the later sixteenth and early seventeenth century.

30 A CORNER OF PIERRE CROZAT'S GARDEN AT
* MONTMORENCY

Pen and brown wash over black chalk, with some white heightening. The border in pen and brown ink.
401 × 267 mm
Paris, Institut Néerlandais, Fondation Custodia (3787)

Provenance: P.-J. Mariette (Lugt 1852: sale, Paris, 1775, part of lot 1284, bt. Mariette's son); E. Rodrigues (Lugt 897: sale, Paris, 28 November, 1928, lot 150, bt. F. Lugt); F. Lugt (Lugt 1082).

Literature: Blanc, 1857, i, p. 293; Schneider, 1932, p. 285; *Le dessin français dans les collections hollandaises*, exh. Paris-Amsterdam, 1964, no. 76, pl. 57; Bean, 1964, pp. 293 ff., pl. 42; *Le Cabinet d'un Grand Amateur, P. J. Mariette*, exh. Paris, 1967, no. 299; Schneider and Ekkart, 1973, p. 285.

Inscribed by the draughtsman in pen and ink, top left: *Dans le Jardins de. M. Crozat à Montmorenci. 1724.*

At the end of the seventeenth century the château of Montmorency belonged to Louis XIV's *premier peintre*, Charles le Brun. There are drawings of it at that time by Israel Silvestre in the Louvre. It subsequently came into the possession of the great collector Pierre Crozat (1661–1740) who entertained his friends there. Mariette observed, of a composition by Watteau etched by the younger Crépy under the title *La Perspective*, that the background was a view of the garden of the château (MS notes in Bibliothèque Nationale, Cabinet des Estampes, under 'Watteau'). Lot 1284 in Mariette's sale in 1775 consisted of 'four views drawn from nature in 1724 in the garden of M. Crozat at Montmorenci' by 'P. J. Mariette, amateur'. Lot 153 consisted of eight copies by him after landscape drawings by Guercino; one of these is also in the collection of the Foundation Custodia (5223; repr. *Apollo*, civ (1976) p. 124, fig. 1.

JACQUES-ANDRE PORTAIL

(Brest 1695 – Versailles 1759)

Portail began his career in Nantes by following his father's profession of architect and engineer, but in about 1735 his reputation as a talented and productive draughtsman gained him a place on the staff of Orry de Vignory, the Comptroller General of the Royal Finances and Surveyor of Building Works. He was appointed draughtsman to the King at Versailles and in 1740 Keeper of the Royal Maps and Pictures, of which he began an inventory in 1743. He also organized annual exhibitions in the Louvre and the Palais du Luxembourg. In 1746 he was put in charge of the drawing-office which made reduced-scale copies of the plans and drawings for the royal palaces (Chennevières, 1898, p. 322). As a painter he was chiefly known for his pictures of still-life, flowers and fruit, and in the same year was elected to the Académie Royale de Peinture. His particular enthusiasm was for drawing, however, and it is drawings – mostly *genre* subjects or figure-studies in red chalk or *aux trois crayons*, in the direct line of descent from Watteau – that constitute the greater part of his *oeuvre*.

Portail was one of the group of artists that gathered round Oudry at Arcueil (see no. 27); it was no doubt there that he came to know Natoire, whose correspondence testifies to his interest in sketching directly from nature (Correspondence des Directeurs, x, 5 July 1752, p.396).

31 THE AQUEDUCT AT ARCUEIL

* Black chalk with some red chalk and pen and black ink.
272 × 421 mm
Paris, Institut Néerlandais, Fondation Custodia (7643)
Provenance: Paignon-Dijonval? (Benard cat., 1810, no. 3728?); Messrs Cailleux; F. Lugt (L 1028), acquired in 1962.
Literature: Le dessin français dans les collections hollandaises, exh. Paris-Amsterdam, 1964, no. 69, pl. 53; Carlson, 1966, p. 159; *Watteau*, exh. Paris, 1968, no. 119; *Franse Tekenkunst van de 18de eeuw*, exh. Amsterdam, 1974, no. 93; Méjanès, 1976, p. 139, fig. 8.
This view in the Prince de Guise's park at Arcueil, a spot much frequented by Oudry and his circle in the 1740's (see no. 27), shows the aqueduct built *c.* 1620 across the valley of the river Bièvre to bring water to the Jardins du Luxembourg. A drawing by Boucher in the Albertina, engraved by P.-Q. Chedel under the title

Le Pont rustique, shows essentially the same view; and two other drawings by him (Fondation Custodia, Méjanès, 1976, p. 138, fig. 1 and Art Institute of Chicago, *Dessins français de . . . Chicago*, Paris, 1976–7, no. 8, repr.) are of the same footbridge but seen from the other side, with the artist's back to the aqueduct. A painting of the aqueduct by Oudry is in the Museum at Schwerin (see no. 27).

It is interesting to compare this drawing with the better-known views of Arcueil by Oudry. The combination of black and red chalk is characteristic of Portail, as is the delicate and nervous precision of the handling. Though he was primarily, a figure-draughtsman, he made landscape drawings throughout his career from his earliest days in Nantes: a view of Nantes has recently been acquired by the Musée Dobrée there (repr. *Revue du Louvre*, 1976, p. 449, no. 4) and there are two views in gouache of the gardens at Versailles in the Musée de Versailles.

NICOLAS-CHARLES SILVESTRE
(Versailles 1699 – Versailles 1767)

He was the grandson of Israel Silvestre (see no. 3), who included many artists among his descendants, and son of Israel's eldest son Charles-François (b. 1667), likewise a draughtsman and engraver. His mother was a daughter of the official clockmaker to the Académie des Sciences and to the Royal Observatory. Nicolas-Charles's talents evidently developed early, for he was still very young when he succeeded to his father's posts, in 1714 becoming drawing-master to the royal pages and three years later to the King himself. In 1738 Louis xv appointed him drawing-master to the royal children. In 1747 he was elected to the Académie de Peinture and in 1752 unsuccessfully applied to succeed Charles-Antoine Coypel as Curator of the Royal Collection of Drawings. Like his uncle, Louis Silvestre the Elder (1669–1740), he specialized in landscape drawings, for which his preferred medium was red chalk (see *Revue de l'Art français ancien et moderne*, 7 July 1886 and *Bulletin des Beaux-Arts*, 10, 1885–6, pp. 115 f.).

32 LANDSCAPE WITH A RIVER

Red chalk.
180 × 322 mm
Paris, École des Beaux-Arts (1546)

Provenance: Le Sougaché, by whom presented in 1891.

Inscribed on the old mount in pen, lower right: *Attr. à N. Ch. de Silvestre.*

Though the events of Silvestre's official career are on record, there is little or no evidence for his stylistic formation and development. But he is known to have made an important collection of drawings and prints, and the present drawing clearly reflects the influence of the seventeenth-century Bolognese school of landscape.

CHARLES-JOSEPH NATOIRE

(Nîmes 1700 – Castel Gandolfo 1777)

A painter of exceptional versatility, who could turn his hand to any kind of subject, whether religious, historical, mythological or allegorical, as well as to portraiture and landscape, Natoire achieved a success equalled only by Boucher's in the period between 1730 – the year of his return to Paris from Rome, where he had been a *pensionnaire* at the French Academy since 1721 – and 1751 when he returned to Rome as Director of the Academy. Among the many commissions he carried out for private patrons and for Louis XV were decorations in the Bibliothèque Royale (now Nationale) and the Hôtel Soubise (Archives Nationales) in Paris, the château of Orry de Vignory at La Chapelle-Godefroy near Troyes, the royal château at Marly and the Queen's bedroom at Versailles. He also made designs for tapestry, including the *Don Quixote* series for the Beauvais factory and that of *Antony and Cleopatra* for the Gobelins. After his return to Rome, he painted a large fresco of the *Death and Glorification of St Louis* on the vault of the nave of the French church, S. Luigi dei Francesi.

Natoire's talent for landscape was greatly appreciated by his contemporaries. It was mainly displayed in drawings, of which a large number and variety exist. Nicolas Vleughels, Director of the French Academy in Rome at the time when Natoire was a *pensionnaire*, first encouraged him in this direction, and during his twenty years in Paris, Natoire was one of the group of artists who frequented and sketched in the gardens at Arcueil (see no. 27). But the greater part of his landscape drawings are the views of Rome and the surrounding country which belong to the period after his return there in 1751, and which occupy an intermediate position between the naturalism of Oudry and the more artificial and romantically 'archaeological' landscape of Hubert Robert. The principal collections of these are in the Louvre, the Musée Atger in Montpellier, the Albertina in Vienna and the Kunstbibliothek in Berlin.

33 A GARDEN AT FRASCATI

Black and red chalk with pen and brown and grey wash.

226 × 336 mm

Louvre, Cabinet des Dessins (RF 14,892)

Provenance : Comte de l'Espine; his daughter, Princesse de Croÿ, by whom presented in 1930.

Literature : Duclaux, 1975, no. 55, repr. p. 39.

Inscribed in pen, lower right: *C de fresca . . .*; signed and dated in pen on the *verso : à Frascati C. Natoire 1755.*

When Natoire arrived in Rome towards the end of 1751 to take up his position as Director of the French Academy, Frascati was one of the first places he visited in search of suitable subjects for landscape drawings (see his letters to Marigny of June and October 1752: *Correspondance des Directeurs*, x, pp. 393 and 415). The series of views that he made there in the 1750's are in fact some of his earliest Italian landscapes. In them he developed what was for him a new technique, combining black and red chalk with pen and brown ink and wash, sometimes adding touches of watercolour.

He used watercolour more extensively for large-scale finished drawings (e.g. no. 36), but these lack the spontaneity of his sketches, among which the views of Frascati occupy an important place. The best-known group of these, dated between 1756 and 1758, is in the Musée Atgar in Montpellier (*Dessins du Musée Atger*, exh. Paris 1974–5, nos. 29, 30; *Natoire*, exh. Troyes-Nîmes-Rome, 1977, no. 72, repr.). Others, dated between 1755 and 1762, are in the Boston Public Library, the Pierpont Morgan Library and the Metropolitan Museum.

Fragonard and Hubert Robert, when they were *pensionnaires* at the French Academy between 1754 and 1763, were encouraged by Natoire to make many drawings on the spot at Frascati.

34 THE RUINS OF THE PALACE OF THE CAESARS ON THE PALATINE

Red chalk and pen and brown and grey wash over black chalk, heightened with white, on blue paper.

292 × 471 mm

Louvre, Cabinet des Dessins (31,383)

Provenance: P.-J. Mariette (Lugt 1852: on his mount, with the inscription: *Reggiae Augg. Domus Vestigia in Hortis Farnesianis sub Monte Palatino Romae delineabat* [in the cartouche] CAROLUS NATOIRE: sale, Paris, 1775, part of lot 1301, bt. for the Royal Collection).

Literature: Tauzia, 1888, no. 2148; Boyer, 1949, no. 592; *Amis et Contemporains de Mariette*, exh. Paris, 1967, no. 53; Duclaux, 1975, no. 57, repr. p. 41.

Signed and dated lower right in pen: *C. Natoire f. 1759.*

This drawing and no. 35, both dated 1759, formed part of a consignment sent to Marigny in that year. In a letter dated 30 May Natoire told him that he was sending four drawings, of which two were for him and two for Mariette *(Correspondance des Directeurs,* xi, pp. 279, 282). It is these last that are now in the Louvre. This drawing represents the ruins of the Palace of the Caesars on the Palatine Hill, then overgrown with foliage and partly transformed into stables. In the foreground are the kind of figures – herdsmen with animals and women and children – that Natoire must often have seen in the Forum, or, as it was then called, the Campo Vaccino.

The emphasis on the ruins is characteristic of the shift of taste that took place in the second half of the eighteenth century. Panini, the famous Italian *vedutista* who specialized in subjects with architecture and ruins, had a great influence on the French artists in Rome. Natoire owned a large number of drawings by him (lots 146–93 in his posthumous sale, Paris, 1778) and also procured them for Marigny and Mariette, his patrons in Paris.

35 THE FARNESE GARDENS ON THE PALATINE
*
Red chalk and pen and brown and grey wash over black chalk, heightened with white, on blue paper.
290 × 471 mm
Louvre, Cabinet des Dessins (31,382)

Provenance: P.-J. Mariette (Lugt 1852: on his mount, with the inscription: *Reggiae Augg. Domus Vestigia in Hortis Farnesianis sub monte Palatino Romae delineabat* [in the cartouche] CAROLUS NATOIRE: sale, Paris, 1775, part of lot 1301, bt. for the Royal Collection).

Literature: Tauzia, 1888, no. 2147; Boyer, 1949, no. 593; *L'Italia vista dai Pittori Francesi,* exh. Rome-Turin, 1961, no. 245; *Amis et Contemporains de Mariette,* exh. 1967, no. 248; Duclaux, 1975, no. 56, repr. p. 40.

Signed and dated lower right in pen: *C. Natoire 1759.*

Natoire owned a garden, probably with a little house, at the foot of the Palatine Hill, which he used as a suburban retreat and where he brought together a collection of Antique sculpture which he encouraged his pupils to study and copy. Many of his Roman views are of the Palatine and its immediate surroundings. The best-known drawing of his garden is in the Musée Atger in Montpellier (*Natoire,* exh. Troyes-Nimes-Rome, 1977, no. 74, repr.). Others of the Farnese Gardens, on top of the Hill, are in the Ashmolean Museum, Oxford (Parker, 1938, no. 533, pl. 68) and in the Berlin Kunstbibliothek (HdZ 3001; Berkenhagen, 1970, p. 240). Both are dated in the 1760's, the most productive period of Natoire's activity.

36 A TERRACE AT NEMI WITH AN ARTIST SKETCHING
Red chalk and pen and brown ink with coloured washes, heightened with white, on (faded) blue paper.
334 × 512 mm
Louvre, Cabinet des Dessins (RF 35,736)

Provenance: H. Prost; N. and J. Prost, by whom presented in 1973.

Literature: Duclaux, 1975, no. 58 bis, repr. p. 43.

Signed and dated to left of lower centre: *C. Nat.! 24 octo.e 1771* and inscribed by Natoire lower right: *il Rumotorio* [i.e. 'hermitage'] *di nemi.*

On 2 October 1771 Natoire wrote to Marigny that he was proposing shortly to go to 'a place called Nemi, near Genzano. I have not yet been there, but I am told that there are beautiful views and these I hope to draw' (*Correspondance des Directeurs,* xii, p. 354). This letter establishes that his first visit to Nemi was in 1771, and that the date inscribed on the drawing has been mistakenly altered to 1761. A number of drawings, some dated 1771 and others 1776, the year before his death, show that he carried out his intention of sketching at Nemi. These are all in watercolour, a technique particularly favoured by the artist in his last years, as his activity as a painter in oils diminished. The two best-known series of such drawings are in the Musée Atger in Montpellier (*Natoire,* exh. Troyes-Nimes-Rome, 1977, nos. 75–6) and in the Albertina. They formed part of the important collection of drawings of places in and around Rome which Natoire made for his own pleasure and also for the instruction of his pupils at the French Academy (*Correspondance des Directeurs,* xi, p. 403) and which were dispersed in his posthumous sale (Paris, 1778, lots 210–56).

FRANÇOIS BOUCHER

(Paris 1703 – Paris 1770)

Boucher's career was one of unbroken and brilliant success as painter, draughtsman, scenic designer, book illustrator, decorative artist and collector; and through the medium of engraving his work became widely known all over Europe. After a short period in the studio of François Lemoyne, one of the leading painters of the 'Rubensïste' school, he came to the notice of the collector and patron Jean de Julienne, for whose publication *Les Figures de différents caractères* (1726–8) he made etchings of more than a hundred drawings by Watteau. The intimate knowledge of Watteau's drawings that he acquired in this way was to have a decisive effect on his own drawing style. In 1727 he accompanied the painter Carle Vanloo to Rome, where he remained until 1731. Though not officially a *pensionnaire* of the French Academy in Rome, he was received hospitably by the Director, Nicolas Vleughels, who allowed him to live there. Soon after his return to Paris he was elected in 1734 to the Académie Royale de Peinture. His *morceau de réception* was *Rinaldo and Armida* (Louvre); but he soon abandoned formal history painting and quickly achieved a reputation as a facile and graceful decorative artist, specializing in mythological subjects, *fêtes galantes* and pastoral scenes (into which he introduced a new element, that of 'bergerie' – the frivolously elegant Arcadian shepherd and shepherdess), treated in a spirit of light-hearted sensuousness. More than any other painter of the period, Boucher typifies the spirit of the Rococo. He became drawing-master to Louis XVI's mistress, Madame de Pompadour, and also adviser on all her artistic projects. In 1765 the King appointed him to succeed Carle Vanloo as Director of the Académie Royale and *premier peintre du roi*.

Boucher was endowed with extraordinary facility, and his versatility was matched by his output: he produced innumerable paintings and schemes of decoration for private patrons as well as for Madame de Pompadour and the King (especially at the royal residences of Versaïlles, Marly, Choisy and Fontainebleau), scenery for the Opera, tapestry designs for the Gobelins and Beauvais factories (of which he succeeded Oudry as Director), book-illustrations and even designs for the decoration of Sèvres porcelain. His interest in landscape dates from his years in Rome, and it was to be an important element in his work throughout his career. He was one of the group of artists including Oudry, Portail and Natoire, who in the 1740's frequented the park at Arcueil and made drawings there (see no. 27), and he also sketched in the country round Beauvais, Charenton and Blois. His paintings of landscape tend to be conventionalized and decorative; but in his landscape drawings there is a sober and at the same time sensitive realism and truth to nature, due partly to the influence of the Oudry circle and partly to that of the Dutch seventeenth-century masters, which make them, to present-day taste, some of the most attractive of his works.

37 VIEW OF TIVOLI
Black chalk.
347 × 222 mm
Louvre, Cabinet des Dessins (24,800)
Provenance: acquired by the Louvre before 1827.
Literature: Guiffrey-Marcel, ii, 1908, no. 1409, repr.;

Jean-Richard, 1971, p. 198, fig. 7; Slatkin, 1972, pp. 399 f., pl. 42; Ananoff, 1946, i, p. 185, fig. 257.

This drawing and its companion, no. 38, were at one time dismissed as products of the studio, but in 1971 the case for Boucher's authorship was stated by Mlle Jean-Richard who pointed out that they are preparatory studies for a pair of pictures painted by the artist soon after his return from Rome in 1731: The *View of Tivoli* in the Nationalmuseum in Stockholm and the *Campo Vaccino*, signed and dated 1734, in the Linsky Collection, New York (Ananoff, 1976, p. 185, no. 48, pp. 228 ff., no. 101, both repr.).

It seems likely that this pair of drawings was also made after Boucher's return, and that they were based on memory and on sketches made directly on the spot. Drawings certainly dateable in the period of his Roman sojourn are uncommon, but there is a view of the cascades at Tivoli dated 1730 and closely related to no. 37 in the Staedel Institute in Frankfurt (Ananoff, 1976, i, p. 185, fig. 256) and one of the Temple of Vesta at Tivoli in the Rijksmuseum (*Franse Tekenkunst van de 18de eeuw*, exh. Amsterdam, 1974, no. 14 repr.).

38 THE CAMPO VACCINO AND THE PALATINE

Black chalk.

345 × 224 mm

Louvre, Cabinet des Dessins (24,797)

Provenance: acquired by the Louvre before 1827.

Literature: Guiffrey-Marccl, ii, 1908, no. 1409, repr.: Jean-Richard, 1971, pp. 198 f., fig. 8; Slatkin, 1972, pp. 399 f., pl. 41; Ananoff, 1976, i, p. 228, fig. 402.

A study for a painting, signed and dated 1734 (see under no. 37). This view was a favourite one among painters and draughtsmen in Rome in the eighteenth century, especially Natoire. It shows the Forum (the Campo Vaccino), and the Palatine Hill with the ruins of the Palace of the Caesars, and on the left the wall and the twin pavilions of the Farnese Gardens. There are topographical inaccuracies which suggest that the drawing was not made on the spot, but from memory. The figures of shepherds in the foreground are clearly inspired by Abraham Bloemart's drawings of which Boucher published a series of engravings, *Livre d'Etudes, d'après les dessins originaux de Bloemaert*, in 1735 (Slatkin, 1976, pp. 247–60).

39 THE COURTYARD OF A COUNTRY HOUSE
*
Black and white chalk.

353 × 479 mm

Paris, Institut Néerlandais, Fondation Custodia (7642)

Provenance: Lord Clive (Lugt 504); J.-P. Norblin de la Gourdaine (1745–1830); in the possession of his descendants until 1958; F. Lugt (Lugt 1082), by whom acquired in 1962.

Literature: Le dessin français dans les collections hollandaises, exh. Paris-Amsterdam, 1964, no. 84, pl. 70; Méjanès, 1976, p. 396, fig. 4.

Signed in black chalk lower left: *f. Boucher.*

Purely architectural subjects treated with this degree of exact realism are unusual in Boucher's work. A view of the same courtyard seen from a different angle is in the Albertina (Ananoff, 1966, no. 612, fig. 107).

JEAN-LAURENT LEGEAY

(Paris c. 1710 – Rome (?) not earlier than 1786)

Legeay was by training an architect: an eccentric and powerfully influential personality, he was one of those architects, not uncommon in the eighteenth century, whose works chiefly existed on paper. In 1732 he won the Prix de Rome for architecture, and spent the years from 1737 to 1742 in Rome. His stay there coincided with a fundamental change of taste among the *pensionnaires* of the French Academy and the group of young artists, including Piranesi, who were closely associated with them. They developed an entirely new artistic language in their drawings of landscape which reflect a novel feeling for the romantic aspect of decaying and ruined buildings; in their fantastic and often unrealizable designs for vases, fountains and tombs; and in their projects for the decorative settings of entertainments and festivities. The medium of engraving, and the dispersal throughout Europe of this generation of artists, gave these architectural fantasies an international currency.

The writings of Cochin, Leblanc and Laugier all bear witness to the great reputation enjoyed by Legeay in the years after his return to Paris, when his pupils included some who were to become the leaders of the first generation of Neo-Classic architects. In 1746/7 he prepared, at the request of Frederick the Great, a set of drawings for a proposed Catholic cathedral in Berlin, and in 1747 he moved to Germany. For the next ten years he worked for the Duke of Mecklenburg-Schwerin, and from 1756 to 1763 for Frederick. In 1768 his presence is established in London where he met the architect Sir William Chambers, who knew his drawings and had made copies of some of them. Between 1768 and 1770 Legeay published some sets of engravings inscribed with titles in Italian, a fact which has led E. Kaufmann (*Architecture in the Age of Reason*, Cambridge, 1955) and J. Harris ('Le Geay, Piranesi and International Neo-Classicism in Rome 1740–1750' in *Essays in the History of Architecture presented to Rudolf Wittkower*, 1967, pp. 189 ff.) to conclude that the engravings were made twenty-five years after the drawings which they reproduce, and that these must have been drawn either in Rome or shortly after Legeay's return to Paris in 1742; and that Legeay can therefore be shown to have exerted a fundamental influence on the formation of Piranesi. Some measure of confirmation for this hypothesis is provided by the fact that a number of drawings by Legeay are listed in the inventory of the effects of Piranesi's son Francesco which were seized by a blockading British warship in 1798 (Archives du Ministère des Affaires Etrangères, Paris: *Rome Correspondance* t.930, fol. 181); but it has been rejected by such recent writers on the subject as Pérouse de Montclos (*Etienne-Louis Boulée*, Paris, 1969) and G. Erouart (*Piranèse et les français*, exh. Rome-Dijon-Paris, cat. p. 182) who will also go more fully into the question in the monograph on Legeay which he has in preparation.

40 FRONTISPIECE FOR A SERIES OF DRAWINGS OR PRINTS OF LANDSCAPES, WOODLAND SCENES AND WATERFALLS

Red chalk.
Diameter 350 mm
Louvre, Cabinet des Dessins (RF 35,517)
Provenance: acquired in 1972
Literature: *Dessins français de 1750 à 1825: le Néo-*classicisme, exh. Paris (Louvre), 1972, no. 2, repr.; *Piranèse et les français*, exh. Rome-Dijon-Paris, 1976, no. 92.

Inscribed on the stone in the centre of the composition, in red chalk: *Varie Inventioni di Paese Bosci et Cascade di Giovani.Lorenso. Le Geay Primo Architetto del Re et intagliate da lui stesso.*

The inscription 'primo architetto del re' enables the drawing to be dated between 1756, when this title was given to Legeay by Frederick the Great, and 1763 when he fell from the King's favour. No corresponding engravings are known, but there is a series of eleven offsets of circular landscapes in red chalk, of comparable size and inscribed with dates ranging from 1757 to 1761, in the Kunsthaus in Zurich. In their bizarre fantasy these compositions seem to be something more than mere capricci, but their significance is obscure.

The grotesque face with extended tongue in the central medallion is characteristic of Legeay's taste for deformed masks. It is probably he who was responsible for a series of caricatures now in the Printroom in Berlin-Dahlem.

JEAN-BAPTISTE PIERRE

(Paris 1714 – Paris 1789)

Pierre's distinguished career gave him a position of great influence in the official artistic life of France in the second half of the eighteenth century. A pupil of Natoire, he won the Prix de Rome in 1734 and from 1735 to 1740 was a *pensionnaire* at the French Academy in Rome. Elected an associate member (*agréé*) of the Académie Royale de Peinture in 1745 and a full member in the following year, he was appointed Professor at the Académie in 1748 and in 1770 Director. In the same year he succeeded Boucher (q.v.) as *premier peintre du roi* and supervisor of the Gobelins tapestry factory. But his influence on painting itself was also significant, and was at least as important as that of his contemporary J.-M. Vien, or that of Carle van Loo in the previous generation.

Pierre was a history painter and not primarily interested in landscape, but like everyone else he made landscape drawings during his years in Italy. These represent a point of transition between the topographical picturesqueness and the complicated techniques in vogue during the period when Vleughels was Director of the French Academy (1725–37) and the simpler and at the same time more analytical style of chalk drawing practised in the 1740's by such artists as Vien and Challe.

The views of *St Peter's from the Vatican Gardens* and *The Church of S. Maria in Aracoeli* in the Albertina (12,248, 12,249) come very close to the present drawing in technique and handling. Other drawings that can also be assigned to Pierre's years in Rome include the seven studies of a fountain, in black chalk, at Darmstadt (HdZ 147–53); a drawing of *Caryatids in a park* in the Witt Collection in the Courtauld Institute, London (4371); one of a *Vase fallen from its pedestal*, in the museum at Orléans (1024 c); and a study of *Trees with ruins* among the anonymous drawings in the Musée Réattu at Arles. Landscapes by him dating from after his return to France are rarely met with, but one example is the red chalk study of *Trees with a ruined aqueduct* in the Musée Grobet-Labadié in Marseilles (1925), dated 1760.

41 THE FOUNTAIN OF THE ACQUA PAOLA IN ROME, SEEN
* FROM THE BACK

Black chalk and pen and brown ink with brown and coloured wash.
196 × 257 mm
Louvre, Cabinet des Dessins (RF 14,848)

Provenance: Comte de l'Espine; Princesse Louis de Croÿ, by whom presented in 1930.

Literature: Méjanès, 1969, p. 428, no. 132.

Inscribed in pen in lower left corner, probably by the draughtsman: *la Porte P. en Rome*; on the old mount: *Mr. Pierre*.

The imposing triple-arched façade of the fountain of the Acqua Paola, built in 1612 by Pope Paul v, is one of the most conspicuous monuments of modern Rome, standing out above the city on the southern end of the ridge of the Janiculum. But with characteristic originality, and in a spirit far removed from that of the conventional Roman view-painter, Pierre chose to draw it from behind at an oblique angle, from the foot of the Porta di San Pancrazio.

A companion drawing, also in the Louvre (RF 14,849), represents one of the small landing-stages of which there were many along the banks of the Tiber before the construction of the embankment at the end of the last century. It is inscribed '*a porta le...*' but does not seem to refer to any of the three gates which are anywhere near the Tiber – the Porta Portese, the Porta Settimiana and the Porta del Popolo (cf. C. d'Onofrio, *Il Tevere a Roma*, Rome, 1970).

JOSEPH VERNET

(Avignon 1714 – Paris 1789)

Vernet received his earliest training in Avignon and Aix-en-Provence, where he achieved some local success as a decorative painter. In 1734 he was sent by one of his patrons to Rome, where he remained for the next twenty years and where he attained an international reputation as a painter of landscape and marine subjects. He was encouraged in this direction by two French painters living there, Adrien Manglard and Nicolas Vleughels (the latter, then Director of the French Academy in Rome, was not himself a landscape-artist but was anxious to foster this branch of art), and also by Vleughels's brother-in-law, the Italian ruin-painter Giovanni Paolo Panini. Vernet, whose wife was the daughter of an Irish officer in the papal navy, found many of his patrons among travelling Englishmen; his studio was a cosmopolitan resort frequented by French and British travellers, connoisseurs, collectors and painters.

Unless a patron commissioned a view of a particular place, Vernet preferred to paint idealized and imaginary landscapes in the tradition of Salvator Rosa and Claude. (He was particularly influenced by the latter's early Seaport compositions.) Contemporary critics indeed compared him favourably with Claude on the strength of what seemed to them the greater range and degree of realism in his treatment of natural phenomena. However fantastic the scene represented, the details of the landscape and the effects of light and weather are rendered with particular care. He made a point of keeping in touch with reality by constantly sketching directly from nature. He told Valenciennes that he had spent his whole life studying the sky, and had learnt something new every day. There is contemporary evidence that he was in the habit of making oil-sketches, thirty-five of which – 'tableaux & études, peints d'après nature, tant à Rome qu'à Naples, de différents grandeurs, sur toile sans cadre' – were included in his posthumous sale in 1790. None of these has so far come to light, but it seems reasonable to assume that they were in the line of descent between Desportes at the beginning of the century (see nos. 6–17) and Valenciennes in the 1780's (see nos. 130–40); they were no doubt as direct, free and vivid as the pen-and-wash sketches of Rome and its environs of which the largest group is in the Albertina in Vienna.

The realistic side of Vernet's art culminated in his most important work, the series of large views of the harbours of France commissioned in 1753 by Louis xv on the suggestion of Madame de Pompadour's brother, the marquis de Marigny, who visited Vernet's studio in Rome in 1750 and who, as Intendant des Bâtiments, was responsible for all official artistic patronage. The series was to have consisted of at least twenty paintings, and in the course of the ten years that followed his return to France he completed fifteen (now Musée de Marine and Louvre), which are among the masterpieces of French eighteenth-century painting; but growing tired of the incessant travelling that the commission entailed he abandoned it in 1762 and settled in Paris for the remainder of his life.

---

42 THE TEMPLE OF VESTA AT TIVOLI
*
Grey wash over pencil.
262 × 379 mm
Paris, Ecole des Beaux-Arts (1589)
Provenance: E. Desperet (Lugt 721: sale, Paris, 1865,

7–13 June, lot 519); A. Armand; P. Valton, by whom bequeathed to the Ecole des Beaux-Arts in 1908.
Literature: L'art français, exh. Paris, 1835, no. 156; *Claude-Joseph Vernet*, exh. London (Kenwood), 1976, no. 53.

Inscribed lower left, in pen: *J. Vernet.*

P. Conisbee (Vernet exh. cat.) dates this drawing not long after Vernet's arrival in Italy, probably *c.* 1737. The temple at Tivoli, always a favourite subject with landscape painters in Rome, occurs in many of Vernet's pictures, and a number of drawings of Tivoli are listed in the catalogue of his posthumous sale in 1790. In Vernet's paintings, the ruins of Antiquity are treated simply as pictorial elements; but they were based on sketches like the present drawing which were made on the spot with an eye for exact detail which studied the subject with the precision of an archaeologist.

43 TWO FIGURES STANDING BY A TREE

Pen and brown ink.
212 × 150 mm
Orléans, Musée des Beaux-Arts (1132.1)

Provenance: Robelot; P. Fourché, by whom bequeathed to the Museum in 1922.

Literature: Le Dessin français, exh. Orléans, 1975–6, no. 115; *Claude-Joseph Vernet*, exh. London (Kenwood) 1976, no. 64; *Joseph Vernet*, exh. Paris (Musée de la Marine), 1976–7, no. 64.

Signed lower right, in pen: *Vernet f! Ro^{mae}.*

This drawing, which seems at first sight uncharacteristic of Vernet, is one of the studies from nature that he was encouraged by Vleughels to make when he was a young man in Rome. As many as fifty-seven studies of trees are listed in the catalogue of his posthumous sale in 1790; this particular one is of exceptional quality in its vigorous pen-work and bold use of wash. P. Conisbee (Vernet exh. catalogue) compares it with the few original etchings by Vernet, in which the influence of Salvator Rosa is also evident – an influence to which Vernet seems to have been

particularly susceptible after *c.* 1746. The drawing may be compared with a study of a tree by Rosa in the Uffizi (*Disegni italiani del paesaggio*, exh, Florence, 1973, no. 65, pl. 51).

44 VIEW OF THE HARBOUR OF NAPLES

Pen and brown wash over black chalk.
294 × 430 mm
Louvre, Cabinet des Dessins (RF 1178)

Provenance: J.-E. Gatteaux (Lugt 852) by whom presented to the Louvre in 1881.

Literature: L'art français du XVIIIè *siècle*, exh. Copenhagen, 1935, no. 527; *Dessins français du Musée du Louvre*, exh. Berne, 1948, no. 53; *Dessins de l'école française appartenant au Musée du Louvre*, exh. Algiers, 1955, no. 88; *Dessins français du* XVIIIè *siècle*, exh. Paris (Louvre), 1967, no. 63; *Amis et contemporains de P.-J. Mariette*, exh. Paris (Louvre), 1967, no. 63; *Claude-Joseph Vernet*, exh. London (Kenwood), 1976, no. 56; *Joseph Vernet*, exh. Paris (Musée de la Marine), no. 65.

Inscribed lower left, in pen: *J. Vernet.*

The absence of figures and the careful treatment of architectural details and boats give this view of Naples something of the dry character of a drawing made for purposes of record; but the rendering by means of a combination of transparent and dark washes of the shadows and reflections cast by the strong southern light is characteristic of Vernet. This drawing may have been made in connection with the celebrated views of the Bay of Naples painted in 1748, two of which are in the collection of the Duke of Northumberland and one in the Louvre (Vernet exh. Kenwood, nos. 7, 8 and 15, all repr.). For other drawings of Naples, see Vernet exh. Kenwood, nos. 57–60, all repr.

AIGNAN-THOMAS DESFRICHES

(Orléans 1715 – Orléans 1800)

Desfriches was trained as a painter, first in Orléans under Jacques Dominé and from 1732 in Paris, first under Bertin and then under Natoire, but the illness of his father compelled him to return to Orléans and enter the family business of importing colonial products. After his marriage in 1743 the life of this collector and amateur painter – as he had necessarily become – was divided between his house in the rue Neuve in Orléans and his country estate of La Cartaudière, near Saint Pryvé, between the rivers Loire and Loiret. The inventories of his collection dated 1752, 1760 and 1774 reveal a taste for Dutch and Flemish painting, which he must have studied during visits to Holland and Flanders in 1753 and 1766. His correspondence (published in 1907 by P. Ratouis de Limay) shows that he was on terms of friendship with such distinguished artists as Boucher, La Tour, Joseph Vernet, Cassas and Wille; portraits of him were executed by Nonotte (1739), Perroneau (1751), Pigalle (c. 1760), Cochin (1765) and Houdon (1777). Though he painted a series of landscapes to decorate his house at La Cartaudière in 1764, his main interest was in drawing. In 1766 he invented a process for making a kind of coated paper, called *'papier-tablette'*, the surface of which permitted an extreme delicacy of execution. His engraved work is limited to four etchings, but his drawings of the country round Orléans were engraved by Cochin, Pâris, Demarteau and Bizemont.

45 THE PONT DE L'ARCHER AT ST-MESMIN

Black chalk.

258 × 398 mm

Orléans, Musée des Beaux-Arts (667)

Provenance: presented to the Museum in 1880 by Mgr Desnoyers.

Literature: Ratouis de Limay, 1907, p. 189; *Le paysage de Poussin à Corot*, exh. Paris (Petit Palais), 1925, no. 405; *Paris et les ateliers provinciaux du XVIIIè siècle*, exh. Bordeaux, 1958, no. 138; *A.-T. Desfriches*, exh. Orléans, 1956–7, no. 137; *Frankreich vor der Revolution*, exh. Münster, 1973, no. 31, repr. p. 177; *Dessins français*, exh. Orléans, 1975–6, no. 32, pl. lxxviii.

Signed and dated lower left, in black chalk: *A. Desfriches 1769.*

A highly characteristic work of Desfriches: characteristic in its subject which is one of the best known places in the country round Orléans, in its technique, and in its evident dependence on Dutch seventeenth-century drawings. Another drawing of the subject by him, on his *papier-tablette*, is dated 1772 (repr. Ratouis de Limay opp. p. 136). An important group of drawings by Desfriches is in the museum at Orléans, notably a large-scale view of Orléans (657; Münster exh. 1973, no. 30 repr.) dated 1761, of which there is an engraving by Cochin and Chauffard.

JEAN-GEORGES WILLE

(Biebertal 1715 – Paris 1805)

Though German by birth, Wille entered the studio of Largillière in 1736 and spent the whole of his career in Paris. He made his reputation as an engraver of portraits, and it was as such that in 1761 he was elected to the Académie Royale. He later made a speciality of engraving the works of the seventeenth-century Dutch and Flemish painters who were then the fashion in Paris; and it was under their inspiration, and that of such friends as his fellow-countryman Dietrich whom he first made known to the French public, that from about 1760 onwards he took up landscape sketching. Most of these drawings were produced in the course of the excursions which he made every summer in the country surrounding Paris accompanied by his sons and pupils. He used to note carefully on them the place and date, and often also the time of day and even the state of the weather. His diary, published in 1857, gives a faithful account of these tours as well as a great deal of invaluable incidental information about other artists in Paris, Parisian collectors and dealers, and German visitors to Paris.

46 A FARMYARD

Black chalk and brown and grey wash.
193 × 305 mm
Louvre, Cabinet des Dessins (RF 29,365)

Provenance: A. Besnus (sale, Paris, 8 March 1922, lot 152); Seymour de Ricci, by whom bequeathed in 1922.

Signed and dated lower right: *J. G. Wille, 1766* and inscribed: *Grange d'une ferme sur la route d'Estampes.*

'On the 31st [of August, 1766] I left Paris accompanied by my son, my pupil M. Pariseau, and by MM. Baader, Freudenberg, and Dunker, all painters. We travelled by carriage and arrived at Longjumeau in time for dinner. I made only two drawings there. The whole of the two next days we spent drawing at Sceaux-Les Chartreux. On the Wednesday we set off in the early morning with a guide for Marcoucy, in order to make drawings of the old castle. We stayed the night there in what is perhaps the most wretched inn in the whole of France; the bugs that we found drove us away by the afternoon. On Thursday and Friday we went again to draw at Sceaux-Les Chartreux and Villers. On Saturday we left again for Paris. On the way I made a drawing at Chamblon and another at Antony.' (J. G. Wille, *Journal*, ed. G. Duplessis, Paris, 1857, i, p. 330.)

All the places mentioned are to the south of Paris and a few miles north of Etampes. This drawing – which clearly reflects some influence of the early seventeenth-century Dutch master Abraham Bloemart – is a typical example of the kind of rapid and unpremeditated sketch that the artist used to make in the course of these excursions. The jagged zig-zag line is characteristic of his handling. Another drawing made on the same occasion, of exactly the same size and in the same technique, inscribed: *J. G. Wille desina* (sic) *pour son dessert, cette partie de l'auberge où il dinait avec ses camarades entre Estampes et Arpageon 1766*, is in the collection of the Courtauld Institute.

44

LOUIS-NICOLAS VAN BLARENBERGHE
(Lille 1716 – Fontainebleau 1794)

HENRI-JOSEPH VAN BLARENBERGHE
(Lille 1741 – Lille 1826)

The van Blarenberghe family, of Dutch extraction from Leyden, settled in Flanders in the first half of the seventeenth century. The father of Louis-Nicolas, Jacques-Guillaume van Blarenberghe, was born in Lille in 1692 and worked there as a painter, dying in 1742. Louis-Nicolas also began his career in Lille, but after the death of his wife in 1751 he moved to Paris where he made his name as a miniature painter. His patrons included Madame de Pompadour, for whom he decorated a snuff-box with two miniatures of the unveiling of the statue of Louis xv which until the Revolution stood in the Place Louis xv, now Place de la Concorde (Blunt, Waddesdon Manor Cat., nos. 117–18), and the duc de Choiseul who shortly after 1760 commissioned him to paint over-doors for the Hôtel des Affaires Etrangères in Versailles (now the Bibliothèque Municipale, where the paintings still are). It was for Choiseul that he executed his two tours-de-force of miniature painting, in which mastery of the technique of painting on an infinitely small scale is combined with extraordinary delicacy of colour: two snuff-boxes, one with views of Choiseul's château at Chanteloup near Amboise, now in the Wrightsman Collection in New York (F. J. B. Watson, *the Metropolitan Museum, New York: the Wrightsman Collection*, iii, 1970, p. 133, no. 8, repr.; A. K. Snowman, *Eighteenth-Century Gold Boxes of Europe*, 1966, pls. 264–6) and another with views of the rooms of his house in Paris, showing his collection of pictures, which even on this minute scale are recognizable, in the collection of Baron Elie de Rothschild, Paris (F. J. B. Watson, *The Charlton Lecture . . . at Newcastle: the Choiseul Box*, 1963; Snowman, op. cit., pls. 377–83).

In 1769 he was appointed Painter in Chief to the War Department and in 1773 Painter in Chief to the Admiralty. Between 1780 and 1790 he was engaged on the series of paintings in gouache of the *Royal Victories* commissioned by Louis xvi, now in the Musée de Versailles (see no. 48).

His son, Henri-Joseph van Blarenberghe, modelled his style so closely upon his father's that their works, which are rarely signed, are difficult to distinguish. From 1774 to 1792 he held the post of drawing-master to the King's children. During the Revolution he retired to Lille, where he opened a school of drawing and in 1803 became Director of the museum. The two artists are best known for their miniature-paintings, but their freely handled drawings in watercolour and gouache show that they also had a remarkable feeling for landscape.

---

47 THE OUTER HARBOUR OF BREST
*

Watercolour, with some bodycolour, over black chalk. 441 × 390 mm
Louvre, Cabinet des Dessins (RF 3496)

Provenance: Mme Henri-François-Alexandre van Blarenberghe, by whom bequeathed in 1907.

Literature: A. F. Blunt in Waddesdon Manor Cat., pp. 234, 287.

Inscribed in pen, top centre: *Vüe prise de la Mature*, followed by a key to the buildings and ships represented: *A. Quai Marchand de Brest, B. Intendance, C. Quai Marchand de Recouvrance, D. Magasin d'Artillerie, E. Casernes des Matelots, F. Forme de Pontaniou, G. Forge aux Ancres, & aux Constructions, H. Capucins, 1. L'Amiral, 2. La Bretagne, 3. La Ville de Paris, 4. Le Rolant, 5. Le Saint Esprit, 6. L'Oiseau.*

The inscription 'vue prise de la mature' explains that this bird's-eye view was drawn from the rigging of a ship, the position of which is indicated by the cross. The drawing is one of an important series of eight watercolour views of the harbour of Brest which Louis-Nicolas van Blarenberghe made in 1773. They were acquired by the Louvre from his descendants in 1907 (RF 3475-6 and RF 3493-7).

A painting in gouache of the outer harbour was until recently in the collection of Lord Rosebery at Mentmore (sale, 25 May 1977, lot 2607) and a box decorated with miniature views of Brest is in the Rothschild Collection at Waddesdon (Blunt, op. cit., no. 123, repr.).

48 THE ENTRY OF LOUIS XV INTO MONS

Watercolour, with some bodycolour, over black chalk. Squared in black chalk. Some details (e.g. a small house in the foreground and a group of figures in the centre) painted over in white bodycolour.
260 × 885 mm
Louvre, Cabinet des Dessins (RF 3479)

Provenance: as for no. 47.

Literature: Gloires Militaires, exh. Paris (Musée des Arts Decoratifs), 1935, no. 349; A. F. Blunt, in Waddesdon Manor Cat., p. 245.

Not only the subject of this watercolour but also its treatment, in which topographical accuracy is combined with freshness of colouring and freedom of handling, place Louis-Nicolas van Blarenberghe in the direct line of descent from his great Flemish predecessor Adam-François van der Meulen (q.v.). The drawing is connected with one of the well-known series of paintings in gouache of the *Royal Victories* which he executed for Louis XVI between 1780 and 1790, now in the museum at Versailles. Its subject is the entry of Louis XV into the city of Mons on 30 May 1747, three weeks after the French victory at the battle of Fontenoy (Pératé-Brière, *Cat. Musée de Versailles,* 1931, no. 417). A replica of the finished gouache, formerly belonging to Baron Edmond de Rothschild, is now in an English collection (see Blunt, op. cit., p. 245).

49 THE FERRY

Watercolour, with some bodycolour, over black chalk. Squared in black chalk.
464 × 929 mm
Louvre, Cabinet des Dessins (RF 3482)

Provenance: as for no. 47.

Literature: A. F. Blunt, in Waddesdon Manor Cat., p. 248.

This important watercolour was attributed to Henri-Joseph van Blarenberghe by family tradition. It is connected with a painting on copper in the museum at Agen, dated 1771, of the château of Veretz on the river Cher, not far from Tours, which then belonged to the

duc d'Aiguillon who in 1770 succeeded the duc de Choiseul as Louis XV's Minister of Foreign Affairs. A painting of the subject in gouache, until recently in the collection of Lord Rosebery at Mentmore (sale, 25 May 1977, lot 2605, repr.), is signed '*V. Blarenberghe né en 1741*': as Blunt points out, Henri-Joseph used this form of signature in his later years.

50 THE CHATEAU OF JARNAC, NEAR ANGOULEME

Gouache.
140 × 203 mm
Louvre, Cabinet des Dessins (RF 3484)

Provenance: as for no. 47.

Literature: Aquarelles de 1400 à 1900, exh. Paris (Orangerie), 1936, no. 1; A. F. Blunt, in Waddesdon Manor Cat., p. 248.

If, as seems probable, family tradition is correct in attributing this drawing to Louis-Nicolas, he must at some time have made a tour in south-west France. A view of La Rochelle by the same hand is in the Rothschild Collection at Waddesdon. (Blunt, op. cit., no. 114, repr.)

51 HOUSES BESIDE A RIVER, BY MOONLIGHT

Gouache.
148 × 244 mm
Louvre, Cabinet des Dessins (RF 3485)

Provenance: as for no. 47.

This drawing in gouache, traditionally attributed to Henri-Joseph van Blarenberghe, reflects the influence of the Dutch seventeenth-century landscape painters, particularly Aert van der Neer who was celebrated for his moonlight scenes. In his later years, Henri-Joseph turned his hand to *pastiches* of the Dutch *genre* subjects of that period.

52 A POLICE-RAID ON A BAWDY-HOUSE

Gouache.
314 × 402 mm
Louvre, Cabinet des Dessins (RF 3487)

Provenance: as for no. 47.

Traditionally attributed to Henri-Joseph van Blarenberghe. The dress of the figures suggests a date *c.* 1780.

53 PANORAMIC VIEW OF A VILLAGE

Watercolour and bodycolour over black chalk, squared in black chalk.
152 × 550 mm. The lower edge irregularly trimmed.
Louvre, Cabinet des Dessins (RF 3491)

Provenance: as for no. 47.

Inscribed in black chalk top right (almost rubbed away): . . . . *gauche, côté ville* . . . Traditionally attributed to Henri-Joseph van Blarenberghe.

JEAN-BAPTISTE LALLEMAND

(Dijon 1716 – Paris 1803)

Lallemand was self-taught, but various influences can be detected in his style: the most obvious are those of Claude Lorrain and Joseph Vernet, Piranesi, and the Italian *vedutisi*, especially Panini whom he had met when he was in Italy from 1744 onwards. He also responded to the art of such seventeenth-century Dutch painters as Wouvermans and Berchem. It was in Rome that he acquired his taste for Antique monuments and ruins. On his return to France he worked in Paris and in Dijon, and collaborated with Greuze. In 1773 he visited London and exhibited at the London Society of Artists. Most of his landscapes, whether in oil, gouache or watercolour, are of confected compositions, picturesque rather than archaeologically exact. But that he was capable of representing a given spot is shown by some of the drawings that he made in Italy and France, especially the views of the landscape and monuments of Burgundy, Franche-Comté, the Lyonnais and the Ile-de-France that he made for La Borde's *Voyage pittoresque de la France* (1781–4).

54 THE 'THEATRE DES ELEVES DE L'OPERA' IN PARIS

Gouache.

410 × 630 mm

Paris, Musée Carnavalet (D. 5978)

Literature: Trois siècles de dessin parisien, exh. Paris (Musée Carnavalet), 1946, no. 189.

Signed in pen, lower left: *lallemand fe.*

An engraving of this view by Denis Née after a drawing by Lallemand is entitled *Vue de l'Ambigu Comique.* P. de Lavaissière pointed out, however, that the building represented is the rehearsal theatre for the training school of the Opéra, which was opened in 1779 in the Boulevard du Temple, opposite the rue Charlot. After being damaged by fire in 1798 it was finally demolished in 1838. The Ambigu Comique was another theatre in the same street (see La Borde, *Voyage pittoresque de la France: Ile de France*, Monuments de Paris, no. 68).

JOSEPH-MARIE VIEN

(Montpellier 1716 – Paris 1809)

Vien began his artistic career in humble circumstances, as a decorator of faience, after which he studied under a local artist, Giral. He also designed the catafalque for the obsequies in Montpellier of the duc du Maine (d. 1736). In 1741 he entered the studio of Natoire in Paris. Three years later, having won the Prix de Rome with a painting of an Old Testament subject (Ecole des Beaux-Arts), he was sent to Rome as a *pensionnaire* at the French Academy. He was much influenced by the then Director of the Academy, Jean-François de Troy; but his principal interest in Rome, apart from making studies from nature, was the then neglected painting of the seventeenth-century Roman and Bolognese schools, particularly Guercino – at that period an unusual object of admiration. He returned to Paris in 1750 and in the following year was elected an associate member (*agréé*) of the Académie Royale de Peinture and in 1754 a full member. His paintings of subjects from the Antique treated in a classicizing vein, such as the *Marchande d'amours* (Fontainebleau) exhibited in the Salon of 1763, made him one of the principal forerunners of the Neo-Classic movement. In 1775 he succeeded Natoire as Director of the Academy in Rome, where he remained until 1781. Like the archaeologist Winckelmann and the German painter Raphael Mengs, he played a leading part in the Neo-Classic revival of interest in Antique art in Rome. He received many official honours under the Consulate and Empire: in 1799 he was made a Senator; in 1802 decorated with the Légion d'Honneur; and in 1808 given the title of Count. Vien's particular importance was as a teacher. In this respect, as Diderot said, he had no rival. His pupils included Regnault, Suvée, Vincent and above all Jacques-Louis David, and he has been justly called 'the re-establisher of the French School'.

55 A WATERFALL IN AN ITALIAN VILLAGE

Black chalk, heightened with white, on blue paper.
292 × 437 mm
Rouen, Musée des Beaux-Arts

Provenance: J. Dupan (Lugt 1440: sale, Paris, 1840, 26 March); H. Baderou (presented by Henri and Suzanne Baderou to the Rouen Museum in 1976).

Inscribed lower right, in pen: *Vanase* (?)

If this inscription refers to the place represented, we have been unable to identify it; but the shape of the roofs and chimneys and the tufaceous appearance of the ground suggest that it may have been Italy, probably somewhere north of Rome.

Vien's activity as a landscape-draughtsman is attested by the number of such drawings listed in the catalogue of his posthumous sale in 1809 (lots 114 and 145–8). The basis for our reconstruction of this aspect of his art is provided by three drawings, in the same boldly hatched technique, attributed to him when in the Mariette Collection: *The Cascade at Tivoli* (Mme V[iel] sale, Hôtel Drouot, 30 March 1925, lot 152 repr.), *View inspired by the Forum of Nerva* (Musée Magnin, Dijon: 1938 cat., no. 950), and the *Marble Cascade at Terni*, signed and dated 1746, acquired in 1972 by the Fondation Custodia (Méjanès, 1976, fig. 11). Others attributable to him include the companion to the present drawing, in the Baderou Collection, also representing *The Cascade at Tivoli*, of which there is a close variant in the Museum at Quimper (as Anon. French, eighteenth century), and drawings in the Musée des Beaux-Arts at Rouen (as Lemonnier), the Petit Palais in Paris (as Anon. French, seventeenth century), the Academy in Stockholm, and elsewhere. It is noticeable how many of his Italian landscapes are of cascades or waterfalls.

MICHEL-ANGE CHALLE

(Paris 1718 – Paris 1778)

Challe began his career with the intention of becoming an architect, and this early interest was to be a lasting influence on him. He won the Prix de Rome for painting in 1741, and in 1742 went to Rome where he remained until 1749. He was there at about the same time as Legeay, Vien, Clérisseau and Le Mettay; and together with Clérisseau, L.-J. Le Lorrain, Petitot and Saly, he was one of the group of French artists in close contact with Piranesi. He and Piranesi exerted a reciprocal influence on one another, and many years later it was he who produced the French translation of Piranesi's writings.

The paintings of architecture and landscape which Challe exhibited in the Salon after his election in 1753 to the Académie Royale de Peinture met with a mixed reception – they did not gain the approval of Diderot, the most influential critic of the day – but on the strength of them he was, in 1758, appointed Professor of Perspective at the Académie. In 1764 he was made Draughtsman in Ordinary to the King, in which capacity he designed theatrical scenery and settings for entertainments and court ceremonies in the scenographic style that he and his contemporaries had evolved in Rome under the inspiration of the Bibienas and Piranesi.

The catalogue of the exhibition of *British Artists in Rome* held at Kenwood in the summer of 1974, laid stress on the links between the English and French landscape artists working in Rome in the years around 1750. Mr Brinsley Ford, in his book *The Drawings of Richard Wilson* (1951, pp. 25 f.), was the first to point out the resemblance between Wilson's drawings in black chalk heightened with white on tinted paper and those by Challe and L.-G. Blanchet, the court painter to the Young Pretender. Challe left Rome three years before Wilson's arrival, so the direct influence is more likely to have been from Blanchet. The latter is still something of an unknown quantity as a personality and as an artist, but in his Roman landscape drawings he comes very close to Challe (cf. a drawing in the Courtauld Institute: *France in the Eighteenth Century*, exh, London, 1968, no. 23).

56 THE VILLA D'ESTE AT TIVOLI: THE 'ROMETTA'

Black chalk heightened with white on blue paper.
326 × 460 mm
Louvre, Cabinet des Dessins (RF 13,924)

Provenance: Comte de l'Espine; his daughter, Princesse Louis de Croÿ, by whom presented in 1930.

Hitherto attributed to Michallon, under whose name it entered the Louvre in 1930, this drawing is in fact by Michel-Ange Challe. The technique, typical of him, is that of the views of the Villa d'Este described in the catalogue of his posthumous sale in 1778 (Paris, 9 March etc., lots 25, 30, 35, 55, 58, 116). But the attribution does not rest solely on technique: the whole style of the drawing with the building up of the composition in simple planes, the strong contrasts of black and white chalk, the emphasis on dark hollows, the dramatic outlines inspired by Salvator Rosa, are all characteristic of Challe. A similar drawing, signed by him, is in the Albertina (12653), and there are two, also

signed, in the Musée Magnin in Dijon (*Dessins français du XVIIIè siècle*, exh. Dijon [Musée Magnin] 1977, nos. 8–9, one repr. pl. vi).

The scene represented is the south-west corner of the Villa d'Este at Tivoli, a favourite subject among artists in Rome. The 'Rometta' is the curious group of fountains in the garden symbolizing Roman rivers and monuments. The waterfall represents the cascades of the Aniene at Tivoli and is surmounted by a miniature version of the circular Temple of the Sibyl. A view by Challe of the temple itself is at Besançon (D. 1559).

Challe is best known for his large drawings of architectural compositions in the manner of Piranesi. His less conventional studies from nature, which include views of the Palatine, the Colosseum and the Roman campagna as well as drawings of rocks, caves and quarries – subjects that particularly appealed to him – reflect the reaction against the traditional 'ruinscape' which took place towards the end of the 1740s.

CLAUDE-HENRI WATELET

(Paris 1718 – Paris 1786)

Watelet was born a rich man, having inherited the right of farming the taxes in the district of Orléans, and was able to devote himself to art and literature. Not content to be a mere amateur, he turned himself into an engraver of fully professional standards. He became an honorary associate of the Académie Royale in 1747 and an honorary member in 1766, having in 1760 been elected to the Académie Française on the strength of his didactic poem *L'Art de peindre*. Some of the articles on painting and engraving in the Encyclopedia (reprinted in Panckoucke's *Dictionnaire Pratique des Beaux-Arts*, Paris, 1788–91) were also contributed by him.

A friend of Marmontel and d'Alembert (though Diderot dismissed *L'Art de peindre* as of little value) Watelet was an early advocate of the 'return to nature' which played an important part in the development of the Romantic Movement in the later eighteenth century. He was also one of the pioneers in France of landscape-gardening. In 1764 he published his *Essai sur les Jardins*, the principles of which he put into practice in laying out his country estate 'Le Moulin Joli'. Watelet seems to have derived his taste for picturesque nature less from 'Capability Brown' and the other English enthusiasts for landscape-gardening, than from his visits to Italy in 1764 and the places he visited and sketched there in company with Mme le Comte, La Vallée-Poussin, Weirotter and Hubert Robert.

57 A FARMYARD AT JALLONS
Pen and brown wash.
200 × 312 mm
Orléans, Musée des Beaux-Arts (1143 A)

Provenance P. Fourché (Lugt 1039a) by whom bequeathed in 1922.

Literature: Frankreich vor der Revolution, exh. Münster, 1973, no. 115. repr. pl. 168; *Dessins français du XVIᵉ au XVIIIᵉ siècle*, exh. Orléans, 1975–6, no. 120, pl. XCI.

Signed and dated in ink, lower left: *Watelet à Jallons le 16 juin 1762.*

The directness of observation and simplicity of vision in this drawing reveal the influence of Dutch seventeenth-century landscape and can be paralleled in the work of Oudry, Boucher, Wille and Boissieu. It is interesting to compare this simple farmyard with the elaborate project for a model farm in Watelet's *Art des Jardins*, in which the sincere love of the countryside felt – as we are now beginning to recognize – by the men of the eighteenth century is overlaid both by the theories that the author derived from his 'Physiocratic' friends (who dreamed of a Utopian existence based on obedience to the 'laws of nature') and by the refined sophistication of his own taste in architecture and landscape-gardening.

JACQUES-CHARLES OUDRY
(Paris 1720 – Lausanne 1772)

Little is recorded about the life of Jean-Baptiste Oudry's son and pupil Jacques-Charles. Though he combined the tradition of his father with a precision of detail derived from the study of Dutch painting, he tended to specialize less in landscape than in painting of flowers, still-life and animals. He worked in Paris, where he was elected to the Académie Royale in 1748 and exhibited at the Salon between 1748 and 1761; but much of his career was spent in Brussels where he lived for many years as court-painter to the Governor of the Austrian Netherlands, Prince Charles of Lorraine.

58 A VILLAGE AMONG TREES BY A RIVER

Black chalk.
323 × 463 mm
Louvre, Cabinet des Dessins (31,433)
Provenance: J. Ehrmann, by whom presented in 1964.
Literature: Duclaux, 1975, no. 293, repr. p. 158.

Signed and dated lower left: *J. C. Oudry 1772.*
Though the influence of the elder Oudry and of Dutch landscape is apparent in this drawing, there is a feeling for the decorative aspect of the picturesque that is characteristic of the later part of the century.

JACQUES-LOUIS CLERISSEAU
(Paris 1721 – Auteuil 1820)

Clérisseau was trained as an architect under J. F. Blondel at the Académie Royale d'Architecture. In 1746 he won the Grand Prix for architecture and in 1749 went to the French Academy in Rome where he remained until 1754. In Rome he was in contact with Panini, Piranesi and the German archaeologist Johann Joachim Winckelmann. On his way back to France in 1754 he stopped in Florence where he met the Scottish architect Robert Adam, seven years his junior, who was on his way to Rome. Adam persuaded Clérisseau to return there with him and to act as his instructor in architectural theory and drawing. In 1755 he accompanied Adam to Herculaneum and two years later to Spalato on the coast of Dalmatia where they examined and made drawings of the ruins of the Palace of Diocletian. The result of this expedition was Adam's famous book, published in 1764, which was to have a decisive influence on the early development of the Neo-Classic style of architecture in Britain. In 1760 Clérisseau met Robert Adam's younger brother, James, whom he accompanied on a tour of Italy. The third member of the party was the Venetian painter Antonio Zucchi who later came to England and became the principal decorative painter in the Adam studio. Clérisseau's architecture was mostly on paper, but in 1764 he designed a pavilion in the Etruscan style for Cardinal Albani which antedates anything of the kind by the Adam brothers, who found it worth their while to pay him a retaining fee of £100 a year to remain in Italy until the reputation of their own firm was securely established.

In 1767 he returned to France by way of Marseilles, where he stayed for a time to make drawings for a proposed publication, *Antiquités de la France*, of which only the first volume, *Les Antiquités de Nîmes*, appeared in 1778 (2nd ed., 1804). In 1768 he returned to Paris, bringing with him a large number of drawings of Italian monuments and buildings, chiefly in Rome, in the Villa Adriana at Tivoli, in the neighbourhood of Naples, and at Spalato, which were purchased *en bloc* by the Empress Catherine II of Russia in 1779 and are still in the Hermitage in Leningrad (some are reproduced in the catalogue of the exhibition *Piranèse et les Français*, Rome-Dijon-Paris, 1976). These drawings established his reputation as an architectural draughtsman rather than an architect, and in 1769 he was elected to the Académie Royale as *peintre d'architecture*. His later drawings are of the nature of *capricci*, freely based on his Italian sketches and highly finished, often partly or wholly in gouache. They were much admired in England, where he was from 1771 to 1775, working in association with the Adam brothers. (A ruin-piece by Zucchi, dated 1767, in the dining-room at Osterley Park shows knowledge of the composition of one of the two gouaches, now in the Louvre, presented by Clérisseau as *morceaux de réception* on his election to the Académie Royale in 1769.) In 1778 Clérisseau was invited to St Petersburg by the Empress Catherine, who wanted an architect capable of designing a small-scale *maison antique* in the park at Tsarkoe Selo. His project for a gigantic palace was rejected and he returned to Paris in 1782. He does, however, seem to have had a considerable influence on Catherine's less 'visionary' and more practical architect, Charles Cameron.

59 PART OF THE INTERIOR OF THE COLOSSEUM

* Pen and black and brown ink with brown and coloured washes, heightened with white, over black chalk.
265 × 382 mm
Louvre, Cabinet des Dessins (RF 14,733)

Provenance: Comte de l'Espine; Princesse Louis de Croÿ, by whom presented in 1930.

When acquired by the Louvre in 1930 this drawing was believed to be by Claude Lorrain. The attribution to Clérisseau, first put forward by J. F. Méjanès and accepted by T. McCormick, is based on comparison with his drawings of the Colosseum in the Hermitage, which are in the same technique and of much the same size: the texture of the stone is treated in the same way and there is the same dry rendering of the contrasts of light and shade (cf. Hermitage, 2470, 2479–84: 2479 is reproduced in the catalogue of the exhibition *Piranèse et les Français*, Rome-Dijon-Paris, 1976, no. 37).

PIERRE-ETIENNE MOITTE

(Paris 1722 – Paris 1780)

He was primarily an engraver. A pupil of Beaumont, he was appointed Engraver in Ordinary to the King and elected an associate member (*agréé*) of the Académie Royale in 1761 (this gave him the right to exhibit at the Salon, of which he took full advantage) and a full member in 1771 with an engraving of La Tour's portrait of Jean Restout. He produced a number of original engraved portraits, but the greater part of his work was in the field of reproductive engraving. His publications include *La Galerie Royale de Dresde* (1753) and *La Galerie du Comte Brühl* (1754). Many of his prints are after the Dutch *genre* painters who were then in fashion in France, and, of his contemporaries, Lancret, Boucher, Baudoin and especially Greuze.

His children followed artistic careers: his sons Auguste and Alexandre and his daughters Angélique and Mélanie as engravers; his son Jean-Baptiste as an architect; the best-known, his son Jean-Guillaume, became one of the leading sculptors of the Empire period.

60 A WINDMILL BESIDE A RIVER, WITH TWO MEN UNLOADING A BARGE

Black chalk.
217 × 339 mm
Louvre, Cabinet des Dessins (31,334)
Literature: Rouches-Huyghe, no. 10,818.
Signed and dated lower centre, in black chalk: *Moitte inv. del. 1774.*

The minute technique of the drawing is characteristic of an engraver. Characteristic, too, of the period is the contrast between the men on one side carrying heavy sacks of grain to the mill and the charming but somewhat unexpected appearance, on the other side, of the two elegant ladies dressed *à la polonaise.*

PIERRE ANTOINE DEMACHY
(Paris 1723 – Paris 1807)

Demachy, who came from a family of craftsmen in Paris, studied under the architectural painter and architect J. N. Servandoni (chiefly remembered today for his church of St Sulpice in Paris), who had been a pupil of Panini in Rome. He was elected an associate member (*agréé*) of the Académie Royale de Peinture in 1755 and in 1758 a full member on the strength of a painting of the interior of a ruined temple (*Piranèse et les français, 1740–1790*, exh. Rome-Dijon-Paris, etc. 1976, no. 56, repr.). In 1786 he was appointed Professor of Perspective. Between 1757 and 1802 he exhibited at the Salon architectural views and 'ruin pieces', particularly of Parisian subjects or *capricci* on Parisian themes. It is to these that he owes his reputation. Demachy, so far as we know, never travelled outside France, and it is curious that he should have chosen to represent Paris as Panini might have done. His subjects were often of fires (e.g. the opera of the Palais-Royal, and the Hôtel Dieu) or the demolitions necessitated by the programme of clearance and re-building carried out around 1760 (the churches of the Saints-Innocents, Saint Jean-de-Grève, Saint Jacques-la-Boucherie and the Cordeliers, the Hôtel de Rouille etc.) or the new buildings in progress, the successive stages of which can sometimes be exactly dated on the evidence of his pictures (e.g. the opening-up of the colonnade on the east front of the Louvre between 1756 and 1776).

61 THE FAIR-GROUND OF SAINT-GERMAIN AFTER THE FIRE

532 × 790 mm

Paris, Musée Carnavalet (D. 4849)

Provenance: Destailleur (sale, Paris, 1896, 18 May, lot 593 or 594, bought for the Musée Carnavalet).

Literature: Salon of 1763, no. 110; *Dessins parisiens du* XVIIIè *siècle*, exh. Paris (Musée Carnavalet), 1971, no. 66, repr.

Signed and dated on the mount, lower left: *Demachy 1763.*

On the night of 16 March 1762 a fire destroyed the buildings of the Fair of St Germain which had stood since the sixteenth century in the grounds of the abbey of St Germain-des-Prés. Celebrated in verse by Ronsard in 1574, and as the setting of Regnard's comedy in 1695, this famous fair attracted not only traders and merchants but also acrobats and jugglers. In the late seventeenth century its marionette-theatres, which had taken over the repertoire of the exiled Italian Comedy, inspired drawings by Claude Gillot. Rebuilt after 1763, the buildings eventually gave place to the present Marché de St Germain erected between 1813 and 1818 on a design by Jean-Baptiste Blondel.

In the background Demachy introduces the façade of the church of St Sulpice, to which (no doubt as a compliment to his early master) he has given towers in accordance with Servandoni's original design. The central pediment was demolished in 1770. A companion gouache of the same subject was also exhibited in the Salon of 1763 and is now in the Musée Carnavalet, together with two paintings by Demachy, one of the Fair of St Germain on fire and the other of the ruins.

GABRIEL DE SAINT-AUBIN

(Paris 1724 – Paris 1780)

Of the seven children of Gabriel-Germain de Saint-Aubin, all of whom followed artistic careers, Gabriel was certainly the most talented, though his younger brother Augustin (1736–1807) did rise in 1776 to the position of Engraver to the Royal Library. Gabriel was trained as a painter under Jeurat, Colin de Vermont and Boucher; but having three times failed to gain the Prix de Rome he abandoned his hopes of a regular official career and contented himself with membership of the unofficial Academy of St Luke. Very few paintings by him are now known (though there are some in the Baderou Collection presented in 1975 to the Rouen Museum) but his activity as engraver and even more as draughtsman have given him a unique position among the French artists of the second half of the eighteenth century. He had a brilliant mastery of all the techniques of drawing and the true journalist's indefatigable curiosity and instinct for the significant detail. In his sketches and notebooks – more than 1,100 drawings by him are listed in Dacier's catalogue (1931) – he recorded every aspect, great and small, of the daily life of the Paris of his time; and though Paris remained the centre of his interest, his rapid impressions of the outward aspect of the city show that he had a real feeling for landscape.

62 THE WALK ON THE BOULEVARD
*
Black chalk and grey, brown and reddish-brown wash, heightened with white. Some outlines are strengthened in pen and brown ink.
371 × 538 mm
Paris, Institut Néerlandais, Fondation Custodia (3634)

Provenance: S. Meller; Mme J. Klever-Schmidt; F. Lugt (Lugt 1028: acquired in 1929).

Literature: Dacier, i, 1929, pl. vi and ii, 1931, no. 325; *De Fouquet à Cézanne*, exh. Brussels-Rotterdam-Paris, 1949–50, no. 99; *Meisterwerke aus Frankreichs Museen*, exh. Vienna, 1950, no. 108; Boucher and Jacottet, 1951, pl. 71; *Le dessin français dans les collections hollandaises*, exh. Paris-Amsterdam, 1964, no. 98, pl. 82; *France in the Eighteenth Century*, exh. London (Royal Academy), 1968, no. 625, fig. 325; *Franse Tekenkunst van de 18 eeuw*, exh. Amsterdam, 1974, no. 109.

Inscribed lower left, in pen: *Benazeht* (perhaps a reference to a previous owner). Traces of a long inscription, now illegible, top right.

The Grand Boulevard, a wide walk with side-alleys planted with trees constructed under Louis XIV on one of the old ramparts ('boulevards') on the east side of Paris, a little way north of the Bastille, was a much-frequented resort of Parisians during the eighteenth century. (The word is now, by extension, used for any wide tree-lined thoroughfare, even in the centre of a city.) The drawing is dateable *c.* 1760, a period when the artist produced a number of representations of the subject, the most important being *La Parade sur Le Boulevard* (National Gallery: Dacier, no. 530, pl. iv) and *La Réunion du Boulevard* (Perpignan: Dacier, no. 529, pl. v). The latter painting includes some of the same elements as the drawing – the tables under the trees, the two figures in the centre, and the crowded footpath on the right – but the composition is upright in format; as is the etching, also entitled *La Réunion du Boulevard*, by A. J. Duclos after Saint-Aubin, the left-hand part of which corresponds with the drawing. (Dacier, no. 527, pl. xx). Gabriel de Saint-Aubin's brother Augustin also worked there at about the same time, *c.* 1760–1: two drawings of landscape format by him were engraved by P.-F. Courtois with the titles *Tableau des Portraits à la Mode* and *Promenade sur les Remparts de Paris*.

JOSEPH-ANTOINE DAVID,
called DAVID DE MARSEILLE
(Marseilles 1725 – Marseilles 1789)

This painter of the School of Provence seems to have worked exclusively in his native Marseilles. Very little is known of his life, beyond the fact that he was influenced by Joseph Vernet and Salvator Rosa, and was one of the founders of the Academy of Painting in Marseilles. He taught there from 1752 and was Director from 1779 to 1781 (Bouillon-Landais, 1893, pp. 371 ff.). His best-known pupil was Constantin (q.v.). Two marine subjects by him were exhibited in the Salon of 1763. He achieved some reputation with his portraits, and above all as an 'excellent painter of landscapes' (see Parrocel, 1890, ii, p. 237).

63 A ROAD BY A MOUNTAIN-TORRENT

Pen and brown wash over black chalk.
250 × 366 mm
Louvre, Cabinet des Dessins (26,188)

Literature: Guiffrey-Marcel, iv, no. 3399, repr.

Inscribed lower right, in pencil: *David de Marseille*; on the left, also in pencil but gone over with pen and brown ink: *Rose(?) de Marseille*.

Drawings constitute the best part of David's work, and this landscape illustrates the skill with which he used his preferred medium of pen and wash. Other examples are in the museums in Marseilles and Montpellier, and there is also one in the Louvre of *Washerwomen by a river* (Guiffrey-Marcel, iv, 1909, no. 3400 repr.). His paintings and drawings were sold in 1789, the year of his death (Bouillon-Landais, 1893, p. 374).

PIERRE-CHARLES LE METTAY

(Fécamp 1726 – Paris 1759)

The arrival in Rome in 1749 of Le Mettay, a former pupil of Boucher, coincided with the beginning there of the new concept of landscape that followed the deaths of Locatelli and Van Bloemen and the departure of Alessio de'Marchis. Like other French artists in Rome at that time, such as Lallemand, Barbault and Clérisseau, he came under the influence of Panini, Manglard and Joseph Vernet. He is also known to have made at least one copy after Salvator Rosa (Jombert Sale, Paris, 1776, lot 30). The little that remains of Le Mettay's work confirms the judgment of Natoire, the then Director of the French Academy in Rome, that he would be better advised to take up landscape in preference to history painting (Montaiglon and Guiffrey, ix, p. 410). To judge from the relatively large number of his works that were engraved, he seems to have achieved a certain measure of success in the course of his brief career. They were mostly landscapes, *capricci* with ruins, and marine subjects including a series of views of the principal harbours on the Adriatic coast in the manner of Vernet. On his way back to France he stopped in Turin and in Lyons, and in both places received commissions for paintings in churches. An *Adoration of the Shepherds* and an *Adoration of the Magi*, both signed and dated 1755, are in the church at Cherasco, near Turin.

It is interesting to note that Le Mettay was involved in one of the first of the archaeological publications that exerted so great an influence on the art of landscape in the later eighteenth century: according to Mariette (*Abecedario*, iii, p. 386) he was commissioned to take the place of his fellow-pupil in Rome J.-L. Le Lorrain, whose efforts had not given satisfaction, in making drawings from sketches taken on the spot by the architect Leroy to illustrate the book *Ruines des plus beaux monuments de la Grèce*, published in 1758.

64 THE ARCHES OF THE COLOSSEUM
*

Black chalk, heightened with white, on blue paper.
294 × 457 mm
Louvre, Cabinet des Dessins (30,971)

Provenance: comte d'Orsay; confiscated during the Revolution and placed in the museum at Versailles (Lugt 2239: see no. 123); transferred to the Louvre in 1823.

Literature: Guiffrey-Marcel, x, no. 9849; Méjanès, 1969, no. 221, p. 557.

Signed in black chalk, lower left: *A. C. Le Mettais (sic)*.

Ever since the sixteenth century the Colosseum was a favourite subject with Netherlandish and French artists in Rome. They tended to draw in pen and wash, an insubstantial if suggestive technique which persisted down to the time of Gaspar van Wittel (d. 1736) in the early eighteenth century.

M.-A. Challe introduced a new method of representing the Colosseum which was followed by the *pensionnaires* of the French Academy in Rome: his strongly contrasted combination of black chalk and white heightening conveyed more effectively the weighty effect of the great masses of stone, the effect of light through the arches, and the contrast between the massive blocks of masonry and the vegetation which covered them. Challe's vision and technique were not without their effect on the style of Piranesi.

The influence of Challe can also be clearly seen in this drawing by Le Mettay (cf. Wunder, 1968, fig. 3; *Franse Tekenkunst van de 18de eeuw*, exh. Amsterdam, 1974, no. 22, repr.; Dijon, Musée Magnin, 1938 cat., no. 133). The connection between the two artists is further established by the fact that a painting by Le Mettay, described as being 'in the manner of Vernet', was lot 250 in the sale of Challe's collection (Paris, 1778). But Le Mettay's vision was less intense than Challe's: in their careful if somewhat superficial attention to detail his drawings of the Colosseum come closer to Clérisseau's.

NICOLAS PERIGNON

(Nancy c. 1726 – Paris 1782)

No detailed study of Pérignon has yet been attempted, though he is one of the most interesting French landscape artists of his day. He died on 4 January 1782 in his sixty-sixth year (*Proceedings of the Académie Royale*, ix, p. 96), so he must have been born between 1725 and 1727. In 1759 he published a series of engraved cartouches, in 1760 two engravings of flower pieces, and between 1768 and 1772 six sets of six landscapes, all from his own designs. Three undated *Caprices de ruines antiques*, which seem to reflect the influence of Demachy, are probably earlier than the landscapes. He was elected to the Académie Royale de Peinture in 1774 as *peintre dans le genre des vues et des paysages*, though he seems to have preferred drawing to painting. In the following year he exhibited views of Normandy, Holland and Switzerland at the Salon. In 1776–7 he was again in Switzerland, making drawings for Laborde and Zurlauben's publication, *Tableaux de la Suisse*, Paris, 1780–2. At the end of 1778 he went to Italy (see *Nouvelles Archives de l'Art Français*, 1876, pp. 46, 49, 51, 146, and 1905, p. 100) and exhibited drawings of Italian views at the Salon in 1779 and 1781.

65 PANORAMIC VIEW OF THE LEFT BANK OF THE LOIRE, FROM THE TERRACE OF THE CHÂTEAU OF MÉNARS

Pen and black ink, with watercolour and bodycolour.
128 × 357 mm
Louvre, Cabinet des Dessins (32,328)

Inscribed in ink on the old mount: *6ème vue du château de nos yeux Prise du Partere de la terrasse du chateau de Ménar ou l'on voit depuis Chambor jus-qua . . . par Perignon.*

See no. 66.

66 PANORAMIC VIEW OF A BEND IN THE LOIRE NEAR THE CHÂTEAU OF MÉNARS

Pen and black ink and grey wash, with watercolour and bodycolour.
124 × 335 mm
Louvre, Cabinet des Dessins (32,329)

Inscribed in ink on the old mount: *7ème veüe du haut de la rivière prise au bout de la première allé du chateau de Menar . . . par Perignon.*

The château of Ménars is on the right bank of the Loire, not far from Blois. Rebuilt in about 1646, it was acquired in 1760 by the marquise de Pompadour. At her death in 1764 she left it to her brother, the marquis de Marigny, Surveyor General of the Royal Buildings (*Directeur des Bâtiments du Roi*) who thereafter assumed the title of marquis de Ménars. Three other panoramic views of the same place are in the Louvre: no. 65 in the present exhibition; *une 3ème vue du château de Ménars prise sur les bords de la rivière où l'on voit les paysages jusqu'au Blois* (32,327); and *une 8'ème vue de Blois* (32,330). There are also six views of the château itself and its gardens by

Pérignon, which show that he was there on two separate occasions: four can be dated between 1760 and 1764, at the time when two wings and service buildings were being added by Madame de Pompadour; in the other two can be seen the alterations made by Marigny in about 1768 to the attic storeys of the side wings and to the terraces (see Ganay, 1935, pls. 157 ff.)

67 COAST-SCENE WITH FISHING BOATS

Gouache on canvas.
535 × 770 mm
Louvre, Cabinet des Dessins (32,317)

Literature: Fontaine, 1910, p. 136; Demonts, 1913, pp. 79 ff.

Signed and dated on the *verso*, in pen: *N. Pérignon. Paris 1777 nº 111.*

Pérignon was elected an associate member (*agréé*) of the Académie Royale on 25 June 1774 and a full member only a week later, and on each occasion offered a painting in gouache on canvas as his *morceau de réception*. In his book cited above on the collections of the Académie, Fontaine suggests that these were probably two views of Paris; but Morel d'Arleux, in the first (MS) catalogue of the Cabinet des Dessins, which was drawn up before 1827 (viii, p. 220), states that the *morceaux de réception* were the present gouache and its *pendant*, also in the Louvre (32,316). There is indeed no reason why the artist should necessarily have painted them in the year in which they were offered.

The formation of the cliffs and the headdresses of the women suggest the coast of Normandy, but the view may well be imaginary.

68 THE 'TEMPLE OF DIANA' AT BAIAE

*

Pen and brown ink with grey, brown and coloured washes.

243 × 385 mm

Louvre, Cabinet des Dessins (32,319)

Literature: Monuments et sites d'Italie vus par les dessinateurs français de Callot à Degas, exh. Paris (Louvre), 1958, no. 24.

Baiae, to the north-west of Naples near Pozzuoli, was a fashionable sea-side resort in the period of the Roman Empire. The so-called Temple of Diana, like the similar vaulted buildings nearby traditionally identified as the Temples of Mercury and Venus, are in fact remains of the baths attached to the villas which once lined the coast.

A view of the Roman Forum by Pérignon, also dated 1779, is in the Louvre (32,320), and there are six other watercolours of Italian views, five of which are dated 1779 or 1780, in the Musée des Beaux-Arts at Besançon (Cornillot, 1957, pp. 123–8).

JEAN-BAPTISTE-DENIS LEMPEREUR

(Paris 1726 – Paris 1796)

Lempereur's father, Jean-Denis Lempereur (1701–79) belonged to a long-established family of jewellers in Paris, where he became a municipal councillor (*échevin*). He brought together an important collection of pictures, drawings and prints which was dispersed in 1773, and collaborated with P.-J. Mariette (see no. 30) in the publication describing in detail the casting of Bouchardon's statue of Louis XV, which was later destroyed in the Revolution. His son was also an enthusiastic amateur of the arts and likewise made a collection which was dispersed in 1796, after his death. He also compiled a dictionary of artists, the manuscript of which, dated 1795, is in the Bibliothèque Nationale. After the death of Mariette in 1774 the younger Lempereur was entrusted with the negotiations for the purchase of his entire collection of drawings on behalf of the King; when these broke down, he was entrusted with the task of bidding on behalf of the Royal Collection at the sale in 1775/6.

Both father and son were draughtsmen and engravers and their work is not readily distinguished. It is to the son that the group of drawings in the Louvre has been attributed. They reveal a particular interest in landscape and a genuine sensibility.

69 TREES BY A RIVER-BANK

Pen and brown wash and watercolour over black chalk, heightened with white, on greyish-blue paper. 220 × 226 mm
Louvre, Cabinet des Dessins (RF 4763)

Provenance: marquis de Chennevières (Lugt 2072: sale, Paris, 4 April etc., 1900, part of lot 544); G. Brière, by whom presented in 1919.

Literature: Catalogue des dessins . . . exposés au Musée d'Alençon, 1857, no. 109; Chennevières, xxi, pp. 269 f.

Signed and dated in pen, lower left: *Lempereur f. 1771.*

Altogether four drawings by Lempereur are in the Louvre. One, signed and dated 1753 and inscribed '*des bords du Loiret près d'Orléans*' (30605; Guiffrey-Marcel, ix, no. 9112, repr.) and another, signed and dated 1774 and inscribed *à Aubray près Sceaux* (30606; Guiffrey-Marcel, no. 9113, repr.) entered the collection as a result of Revolutionary confiscation. The other two, the present drawing and one of a winding country road (RF 4762), once belonged to the marquis de Chevennières, Directeur des Beaux-Arts from 1873 to 1880, and were given to the Louvre by M. Gaston Brière, Conservateur des Musées Nationaux. A note by Chevennières on the back of the mount of the drawing exhibited reads: 'Drawing by Lempereur, the eighteenth-century collector, which I found on Painel's stall in the Place du Carrousel'; and in the account of his collection which he published in *L'Artiste* he notes that he had seen another sketch of the same place, inscribed presumably by Lempereur, *dans le parc de Levainville.*

JEAN PILLEMENT

(Lyons 1728 – Lyons 1808)

To use his own words (see Pillement, 1945, pp. 18 f.) 'he went to London and studied the taste of the English. Finding that on the whole they prefer landscape to history painting and pictures rather than drawings, he resolved to devote himself to drawing.' After a short period as a draughtsman at the Gobelins tapestry factory, he went to Spain in 1745, when he was only seventeen. His career as a fashionable decorative painter and designer was to take him at intervals all over Europe: from Madrid to Lisbon and then to London (where he stayed for ten years, from 1750 to 1760), Turin, Rome, Milan, Vienna and Warsaw. In 1778, after some decorative work at the Petit Trianon for Marie Antoinette, he was appointed her court painter; but he outlived his vogue and died in poverty some years after the Revolution.

His widespread influence on the decorative arts was in great part due to the publication in 1767 of a large collection of his engraved designs, under the title: *One hundred and Thirty figures and ornaments, and some flowers, in the Chinese style. The remaining seventy prints are of small landscapes and sea-shore views embellished with figures and ornaments, also the Elements, the Four Seasons, the Four Times of Day, and many other agreeable subjects.* This title well defines his scope as an ornamentalist, emphasizing as it does his significance as the propagator of a particularly elegant kind of rococo *Chinoiserie.* As a landscape artist he was highly eclectic. Not surprisingly, his subjects are rarely taken directly from nature (one exception is the series of five paintings of the gardens at Bemfica near Lisbon, now in the Musée des Arts Decoratifs in Paris, which date from his last visit to Portugal in 1785) and a wide range of disparate and largely unassimilated influences can be detected in his landscapes. These include the Dutch seventeenth-century masters, Oudry, Hubert Robert, Marco Ricci and Francesco Guardi; while in his harbour and shipwreck scenes he comes so close to Joseph Vernet as even to be confusable with him (see the excellent article by Lise Florenne, 'Pillement paysagiste en son temps' in *Médecine de France*, 1967). The drawing here exhibited (no. 70) in which elements drawn from naturalistic Dutch landscape are transformed into a highly artificial decorative rococo, is a good example of his more personal style.

70 'LES PLAISIRS DE L'HIVER'
*
Black chalk with pen and black ink and grey wash and some white heightening.
383 × 550 mm
Louvre, Cabinet des Dessins (32,410)

Literature: Audin and Vial, 1919, ii, p. 123.

Signed lower right, in pen: *J. Pillement.*

One of a series of drawings representing the *Four Seasons,* all in the Louvre (32,407–10), which were engraved in London between 1757 and 1760 by Mason, Woollett and Canot under the respective titles: *Les Amusements du Printemps, Les Agréments de l'Eté, Les Douceurs de l'Automne* and *Les Plaisirs de l'Hiver* (Riotot, 1930, v–viii).

Though this drawing is clearly inspired by Dutch seventeenth-century winter landscapes (the inspiration is made quite explicit by the windmills alongside the canal), skating and sledging were also fashionable amusements in France in the eighteenth century. The figures are dressed *à la polonaise,* though this composition, engraved in 1759, dates from before Pillement's stay in Warsaw.

71 TWO ITALIAN LANDSCAPES WITH HERDSMEN CROSSING A FORD

Black chalk.
340 × 260 mm
Louvre, Cabinet des Dessins (32,406)

Literature: Paris et les ateliers provinciaux, exh. Bordeaux, 1958, no. 157; *Amis et contemporains de P.-J. Mariette,* exh. Paris (Louvre), 1967, no. 78.

Both drawings signed in black chalk, lower right: *J.*

Pillement. The upper one is inscribed, in the margin below: *canpangne Prais de Plaisance* [i.e. Piacenza] *34*, and the lower one: *frimian(?) an virons de Boulogne 35*.

Pillement seems to have intended to make up an album of drawings executed in the course of his travels in Italy in 1762–3. A similar drawing in the museum at Poitiers (882-1-97), made in the same part of Italy, is inscribed '*Vue du chemin de Parme à Plaisance 36*'. The numbering suggests that there was a series of at least thirty-six such views, but only these three are now known.

NICOLAS-MARIE OZANNE

(Brest 1728 – Paris 1811)

Nicolas Ozanne is the best-known member of a family of engravers and draughtsmen from Brest who specialized in naval and marine subjects. Trained as a naval engineer, he became drawing-master at the Naval Academy at Brest, but in 1751 he was called to Paris to assist with the production of a series of engravings commemorating the visit of Louis xv to Le Havre. In 1752 he was elected a member of the Académie de Marine, and went on to complete his training in the studios of Joseph Vernet, Natoire, Boucher and the English engraver John Ingram. In 1757 he was appointed Marine Draughtsman to the King, and in 1769 was charged with building a fleet of miniature boats for the lake at Versailles, and with the instruction of the Dauphin and his two younger brothers (later successively Louis xvi, Louis xviii and Charles x) in the rudiments of naval construction and navigation. His official duties also involved him in the design and building of warships and harbour works. A number of albums of drawings by him are preserved in the Louvre and the Musée de la Marine, many of which were made for series of historical or didactic engravings. These included the *Treatise on the Navy*, 1762; three works on ship-building intended for the instruction of the royal princes, 1769 (Louvre; Prache, 1975, nos. 296–8 and 301–33), *The Campaigns of Admiral Duguay-Trouin*, 1770 (Louvre; Prache, 1975, no. 299), and, most important of all, the series of *Sixty views of the harbours of France* commissioned by the King together with *Sixteen views of France and her Colonies*, which were executed between 1775 and 1787.

72 VIEW OF BREST

Pen and black ink and grey wash over black chalk.
332 × 571 mm
Louvre, Cabinet des Dessins (32,105)

Provenance: from a made-up album acquired by the Louvre before 1850.

Literature: Vichot, 1971, B 2a(3); Prache, 1975, no. 332, repr. p. 175.

The view is from a hill overlooking the town to the east. The album from which the drawing came contained views of harbours, including several of Brest and one, dated 1786, of Fécamp (Prache, 1975, nos. 333–41, repr. pp. 175–7). They are connected with the series *Plans, Dessins et Vues des Ports du Royaume* commissioned by Louis xv, for which Ozanne made the drawings between 1775 and 1787. They were engraved by his sister Jeanne-Françoise Ozanne and his brother-in-law Yves Le Gouaz.

The series was one of Ozanne's most important works, and reveals the influence of Joseph Vernet. The drawing exhibited is characteristic in the deliberate balance of the composition, the careful indication of every detail of the town, and the luminous quality of the wash, especially noticeable in the rendering of the great expanse of cloudy sky.

SIMON-MATHURIN LANTARA

(Oncy 1729 – Paris 1778)

Beyond the fact that he was born in a village near Barbizon, on the edge of the Forest of Fontainebleau, nothing is known of the circumstances of Lantara's early life and training. He seems not to have made the customary journey to Italy, or indeed ever to have travelled abroad. He showed paintings in two of the Place Dauphine exhibitions, in 1771 and 1773, but there are few contemporary references to him. Nevertheless he is well represented in French museums, both as painter and as draughtsman. The influence of Dutch seventeenth-century landscape and of such French contemporaries as Julliard is evident in his compositions, which tend to be made up of details studied directly from nature combined with no particular regard for topographical accuracy but with a certain feeling for realism in the rendering of the effects of light. (An exception is the series of twelve *Vues des environs de Paris* which were engraved by Le Bas.) Lantara followed the example of Joseph Vernet and Pillement in often painting pictures in pairs or sets illustrating the different seasons of the year or the times of day.

Lantara died in poverty, and the legend of his hand-to-mouth convivial way of life brought him posthumous fame as the archetype of the traditional 'Bohemian' artist. Three plays on this theme, in which he was the central figure, were produced in the early nineteenth century (see G. Levitine, 'Les origines du mythe de l'artiste bohème en France: Lantara' in *Gazette des Beaux-Arts*, Sept. 1975, pp. 49 ff.).

73 THE HOUSE OF THE DUCHESSE DU MAINE AT THE
* ARSENAL

Black chalk.
238 × 345 mm
Musée Carnavalet (D. 5990)

Provenance: acquired in 1896.

Literature: B. de Montgolfier, 1970, no. 59, fig. 15; *Dessins parisiens du* XVIIIè *siècle*, exh. Paris 1971, no. 55, repr. p. 27.

Signed lower left, in black chalk: *Lantara*.

This drawing is part of Sketchbook no. xiii, of 'Landscapes after Nature by Lantara' where it is entitled 'View of a house adjoining the Arsenal in Paris'; Sketchbook no. xiv contains a view of the front of the same house seen from the river, and no. xv a 'View of the Arsenal in Paris and the powder magazine from the direction of the moat. In the distance, part of the Bastille'. The building on the far side of the river in the present drawing is the Hospital of the Salpétrière.

The house was built in 1729 by Boffrand, after the destruction by fire of the *petite maison* at the Arsenal, for the duc du Maine, the eldest legitimized son of Louis XIV and Madame de Montespan. The Arsenal was the official residence of the Grand Master of the Ordnance, a post occupied by the Duke from 1694 until his death in 1736.

74 IMAGINARY VIEW OF A CASTLE BESIDE A RIVER BY
MOONLIGHT

Black chalk, heightened with white.
290 × 420 mm
Rouen, Musée des Beaux-Arts (868-5-10)

Provenance: A. C. Le Monnier; H. Le Monnier, by whom bequeathed in 1868.

Literature: F. Guéroult, *Dessins du* XVIIè *et du* XVIIIè *siècles au Musée des Beaux-Arts de Rouen* (unpublished MS thesis).

Inscribed in pen, lower right: *Lantara*.

PIERRE-JACQUES VOLAIRE

(Toulon 1729 – Naples c. 1802? or Lerici, c. 1790?)

Born of a family of artists in Toulon, and trained there, Volaire in 1754 met Joseph Vernet (q.v.), who had come to Toulon in the course of the tour of French sea-ports which he was making in connection with the series of views commissioned by Louis XV. Taken on by Vernet as an assistant, for the next ten years, until 1763, he accompanied him on this tour and visited Bordeaux, Bayonne, La Rochelle and Dieppe. In 1764 Volaire moved to Italy, settling first in Rome, until 1769, and then in Naples. Neither the place nor the date of his death are recorded with certainty.

Volaire was one of Vernet's closest imitators, though his pictures are often characterized by an exaggerated emphasis on theatrical effect. One of his favourite subjects was the eruption of Vesuvius – an event which took place more than once in the course of the eighteenth century. The success that such views enjoyed was due partly to scientific curiosity and partly to the proto-romantic sentiment for nature in her most sublime manifestations.

75 HARBOUR-SCENE BY MOONLIGHT

*

Pen and black ink and grey wash. Traces of underdrawing in black chalk.

256 × 505 mm

Louvre, Cabinet des Dessins (RF 3936)

Literature: Joseph Vernet, exh. Paris (Musée de la Marine), 1976–7, no. 66, repr.

This drawing, until recently attributed to Joseph Vernet but identified by P. Conisbee in the catalogue of the Vernet exhibition as a study by Volaire for a painting by Ingersoll-Smouse (1926, i, p. 35, fig. 9, pl. vi) entitled *Clair de lune – vue du Vésuve*, illustrates the persistent confusion between the two artists. The influence of Vernet is evident in the way the wash is used to suggest the effect of light, but Volaire handles it less subtly; and the attribution to him is confirmed by the drawing of the crowd of animated little figures in the foreground.

The title given to the composition is incorrect: the peak in the left background beyond the lighthouse is plainly not a volcano but a headland, on the highest point of which a fortress is indicated. There can be no doubt that the scene is an imaginary one.

JACQUES-FRANÇOIS AMAND

(Paris 1730 – Paris 1769)

A pupil of J. B. Pierre (q.v.), Amand won the Prix de Rome in 1758 with a painting of *Samson and Delilah* (Mainz). After a year at the Ecole des Elèves Protégés (see p. 69), he arrived at the beginning of 1759 at the French Academy in Rome, where he remained until 1763. In 1764 he was elected an associate member (*agréé*) of the Académie Royale de Peinture and pursued the career of a historical painter, with such pictures as *Joseph and his Brethren* (Besançon, where there is also a preparatory drawing; oil-sketch at Quimper), and *Hannibal's brother Magon demanding further help from the Carthaginian Senate* (Saint-Lô, destroyed 1944) which he offered as his *morceau de réception* on his election to full membership of the Académie in 1767. Two years later he committed suicide.

Mariette wrote of him (*Abecedario*, i, p. 138): 'he showed promise, but was by nature so timid and self-effacing that he lost heart and produced very little. Eventually he became so discouraged that he put an end to himself. I have some of the landscape-drawings that he made in Rome, which show considerable talent. He was a pupil of Pierre, and had benefited by the excellent education which his parents had given him. His death was a sad loss'.

His posthumous sale (Paris, 30 June etc., 1769) included more than 1500 drawings of figure-studies and landscapes, as well as a number of sketchbooks. The Italianate views with large-scale figures, in red chalk (e.g. Louvre 23,539; Guiffrey-Marcel, i, no. 27, repr.) are easily identifiable, as are his interior scenes (e.g. Frankfurt, Staedel Institute, 1204), but most of his drawings of pure landscape still go under the name of his friend and contemporary in Rome, Hubert Robert (q.v.).

76 ROME: THE AURELIAN WALL AND THE PORTA
* ASINARIA

Red chalk.
294 × 422 mm
Louvre, Cabinet des Dessins (23,532)

Provenance: P.-J. Mariette (Lugt 1852: sale, Paris, 1775, part of lot 1076, bought for the Cabinet du Roi).

Literature: Guiffrey-Marcel, i, no. 30, repr.; *Il settecento a Roma*, exh. Rome, 1959, no. 1257; *Amis et contemporains de P.-J. Mariette*, exh. Paris (Louvre), 1967, no. 81; *Les joies de la nature au XVIIIè siècle*, exh. Paris (Bibliothèque Nationale), 1971, no. 239.

Inscribed by Mariette in the cartouche on his mount: *Jacob Fr. Amand Romae ad Portam major*. The Porta Asinaria is a gate in the Aurelian Wall, near ('ad') the Porta Maggiore.

Lot 1076 in the Mariette Sale consisted of two drawings, the second of which, of an unidentified street scene in or near Rome, is in the Museum of Art in Indianapolis (*French Master Drawings of the 17th and 18th centuries in North American collections*, exh. Toronto-Ottawa-San Francisco-New York, 1972, no. 1, pl. 118).

77 A MOUNTAIN LANDSCAPE WITH A BRIDGE OVER A TORRENT

Red chalk over black chalk underdrawing.
165 × 225 mm
Louvre, Cabinet des Dessins (23,534)

Provenance: P.-J. Mariette (Lugt 1852: sale, Paris, 1775, part of lot 1077, bought for the Cabinet du Roi).

Literature: Guiffrey-Marcel, i, no. 32; *L'Italia vista dai pittori francesi del XVIII e XIX secolo*, exh. Rome-Turin, 1961, no. 6.

On Mariette's mount, inscribed on the cartouche: *Jacob Franc. Amand*.

See no. 78.

78 A MOUNTAIN LANDSCAPE WITH A WATERFALL

Red chalk over black chalk underdrawing.
163 × 225 mm
Louvre, Cabinet des Dessins (23,534 bis)

Provenance: as for no. 77.

Literature: Guiffrey-Marcel, i, no. 33; *L'Italia vista dai pittori francesi del XVIII e XIX secolo*, exh. Rome-Turin, 1961, no. 7.

On Mariette's mount, inscribed on the cartouche: *Jacob Franc. Amand.*

On his way back to France by way of Switzerland in the summer of 1763 Amand followed his Italian views – some of which were drawn directly from nature and others transformed into pastoral or *genre* scenes by the addition of figures – with a series of drawings of mountain scenery. The two drawings exhibited are from a group of nine landscapes with mountains, waterfalls, chalets, etc. in the Louvre, which are all the same size and all from the Mariette Collection (23,583–23,587 bis). Others, from the P. Fourché Collection (Lugt 1039a) are in a private collection in Paris.

JEAN-HONORÉ FRAGONARD

(Grasse 1732 – Paris 1806)

Though born in Provence, Fragonard was only ten when his parents moved to Paris. At about fifteen he was put to study first for a short time under Chardin, whose teaching he found uncongenial, and then, more successfully, under Boucher. In 1752 he won the Prix de Rome with a painting of *Jeroboam sacrificing to the Idols* (Ecole des Beaux-Arts, Paris), and after spending two years under Carle Vanloo at the Ecole des Elèves Protégés, which had been established to provide some sort of general education for young artists going to Rome, he arrived there at the end of 1756. On the advice of Natoire, then Director of the French Academy (q.v.), and influenced by his close associate Hubert Robert (q.v.), who though slightly younger had already found his own vocation, he began to devote himself to landscape-drawing. In this he was encouraged by his first patron, the Abbé de Saint-Non, who in the summer of 1760 took him and Robert to the Villa d'Este at Tivoli, an experience that was to have a lasting effect on the development of both artists (see nos. 79, 80, 83). On his way back to Paris with Saint-Non in the following year he made a series of small black chalk drawings, mostly copies of works of art in Florence and Genoa, for a projected publication by Saint-Non, '*Fragments choisis dans les Peintures et les Tableaux . . . de l'Italie*'. Seventy-one of these were acquired by the British Museum in 1936. In 1765 he was elected to the Académie Royale, offering as his *morceau de réception* a painting of a historico-religious subject, *Coresius sacrificing himself to save Callirhoe*. In the 1760's he painted a number of landscapes in the style of the Dutch seventeenth century, especially of Ruysdael, and some with rustic figures and animals in which can be detected the influence of Giovanni Battista Castiglione. But he also began to develop a kind of *fête galante*, park-scenes with figures often on a relatively small scale (cf. no. 83). These include *The Swing*, commissioned in 1766 (Wallace Collection), the four large decorative paintings commissioned in 1771 by Madame du Barry for her house at Louveciennes (Frick Collection, New York), the *Fête at Saint-Cloud* (Banque de France, Paris) painted in about 1775, and *The Swing* and *Blind-man's-buff* of about the same period (Washington). In 1772 he went to Flanders and Holland and in the following year, for the second and last time, to Italy with his patron Bergeret de Grandcourt (see no. 82). Not long after his return to Paris in 1774 he abandoned landscape in favour of sentimental *genre* and allegory. The rise of Neo-Classicism made his art seem old-fashioned, and by the mid-1780's his vogue was beginning to wane. During the Revolution he retired to Grasse, but came back to Paris in 1794 where he was appointed (at the instance of J.-L. David) one of the curators of the newly established National Museum, a position which he held for only two years. He died in the first years of the Empire, forgotten by the younger generation.

79 VIEW IN THE GARDENS OF THE VILLA D'ESTE AT
* TIVOLI

Red chalk.
350 × 487 mm
Besançon, Musée des Beaux-Arts (D. 2850)

Provenance: Abbé de Saint-Non; P.-A. Pâris, by whom bequeathed in 1819 to the city of Besançon; transferred in 1843 from the Municipal Library to the Musée des Beaux-Arts.

Literature: Pâris, 1806, no. 113; Portalis, 1889, pp. 37, 304; *Le Paysage français de Poussin à Corot*, exh. Paris (Petit Palais), 1925, no. 431; Feuillet, 1926, pl. 33; Martine, 1927, pl. 21; *Le Dessin français dans les collections du* XVIIIè *siècle*, exh. Paris (Galerie des Beaux-Arts), 1935, no. 263; *Musée de Besançon*, exh. Paris (Musée des Arts Decoratifs), 1957, no. 144; Cornillot, 1957, no. 37 repr.; Ananoff, ii, 1963, no. 891, fig. 235.
It was early in 1760 that the Abbé de Saint-Non first

met Fragonard. In the summer of that year the Abbé took him and Hubert Robert (q.v.) to Tivoli, where he had permission from the Duke of Modena's agent in Rome to make use of the Villa d'Este. The villa was built in the middle of the sixteenth century, and its gardens, on a southward-facing slope with an abundant supply of water, are typical of the period in their combination of fountains and cascades with an elaborate and intricately planned architectural setting. By the middle of the eighteenth century the trees were fully grown, and a long period of neglect had given the garden the same picturesque atmosphere of overgrown, romantic untidiness that had attracted Oudry in the Prince de Guise's garden at Arcueil (see no. 27).

The present drawing and no. 80 are two of the famous series of ten views of the gardens of the Villa in the museum at Besançon (Cornillot, 1957, nos. 32–41), conceived as finished works of art complete in themselves, which Fragonard made on this occasion for Saint-Non. The latter wrote: 'Fragonard is inspired. There is a magic about his drawings that enchants me. He makes them one after another, and I can hardly bear to wait for the next one' (L. Guimbaud, *Saint-Non et Fragonard*, 1928, p. 98). Fragonard returned to Paris in 1761, and these drawings illustrate perfectly the way of drawing and conception of landscape that he had attained by the end of his first visit to Italy. They mark a definite break with the literal realism of the traditional topographical view: the balance they strike halfway between direct observation of nature and picturesque romanticism was to be an essential stage in Fragonard's evolution as a landscape artist. Mariette wrote of them: 'I have never seen such beautiful chalk drawings. In Rome he drew many views, outstanding among which are those of the Villa d'Este, which are works of genius and of great intelligence' (*Abecedario*, ii, p. 263). According to the manuscript catalogue of the collection of their former owner, P.-A. Pâris, they were exhibited at the Salon following Fragonard's election to the Académie Royale in 1765; they must in any case have greatly contributed to his reputation.

The present drawing and no. 80 are two of the famous series of ten views of the gardens of the Villa in *The Villa d'Este at Tivoli*, 1960, fig. 17). It was etched by Saint-Non in his *Raccolta di vedute* (1765) and as pl. xiv, 2 of the *Recueil de Griffonis* (1790). Ananoff lists an offset reworked in pen and ink, and another drawing of the same view but without the figures (op. cit., ii, nos. 892–3).

80 VIEW IN THE GARDENS OF THE VILLA D'ESTE AT TIVOLI

Red chalk.
488 × 361 mm
Besançon, Musée des Beaux-Arts (D. 2845)
Provenance: as for no. 79.

Literature: Salon of 1765, no. 178; Pâris, 1806, no. 112; Portalis, 1889, p. 304; *Le Paysage français de Poussin à Corot*, exh. Paris (Petit Palais), 1925, no. 433; Feuillet, 1926, pl. 34; Martine, 1927, pl. 22; *Le Dessin français dans les collections du XVIIIè siècle*, exh. Paris (Galerie des Beaux-Arts), 1935, no. 259; *Landscape in French Art*, exh. London (Royal Academy), 1949, no. 417; *Fragonard*, exh. Berne, 1954, no. 49; *Musée de Besançon*, exh. Paris (Musée des Arts Decoratifs), 1957, no. 145; Cornillot, 1957, no. 38, repr.; Ananoff, ii, 1963, no. 908, fig. 716.

This drawing belongs to the series of views of the garden of the Villa d'Este made for the Abbé de Saint-Non in the summer of 1760, as no. 79. It represents the Fountain of Pomona, with on the left the entrance to the enclosure containing the Oval Fountain or Fountain of Tivoli and on the right one end of the Alley of the Hundred Fountains (see D. R. Coffin, *The Villa d'Este at Tivoli*, 1960, fig. 29).

The drawing by J.-J. Le Barbier also in the exhibition (no. 116) is clearly of the same corner of the Villa d'Este, with variations introduced by the draughtsman.

81 WASHERWOMEN BY A WALL
*

Red chalk, the ruled border in pen and brown ink.
348 × 482 mm
Louvre, Cabinet des Dessins (26,652)
Provenance: Revolutionary confiscation.

Literature: Reiset, 1869, no. 732; Guiffrey-Marcel, v, no. 4054, repr.; Portalis, 1889, p. 307; Martine, 1927, pl. 3; *Artistes français en Italie*, exh. Paris (Musée des Arts Decoratifs), 1934, no. 462; *Chefs d'oeuvre de l'art français*, exh. Paris (Palais National des Arts), 1937, no. 538; Lavallée, 1938, pl. 2; *Monuments et sites d'Italie vus par les dessinateurs français de Callot à Degas*, exh. Paris (Louvre), 1958, no. 26; Ananoff, i, 1961, no. 317; *Amis et contemporains de Mariette*, exh. Paris (Louvre), 1967, no. 85, pl. xvii; Duclaux, 1968, no. 55, repr.

Inscribed in red chalk, lower right: *frago*.

The scene is traditionally said to have been at Tivoli; and in size, technique and style the drawing belongs with the group of views of the Villa d'Este which Fragonard drew for the Abbé de Saint-Non in 1760 (cf. nos. 79, 80). Natoire, then Director of the French Academy in Rome, wrote to Marigny on 27 August 1760, of Fragonard 'Our young artist is enjoying himself – he has a most refreshing taste for this kind of landscape, into which he very successfully introduces rustic subjects'. He also urged Fragonard and Hubert Robert to go in for the same kind of *'vue animée de personnages'* that he himself had adopted for his views in and around Rome.

The ostensible subject of the drawing is the group of washerwomen – a favourite theme with Fragonard and Hubert Robert – but the focus of the artist's attention is not on these lightly sketched figures so much as on the great ruined and overgrown wall that constitutes the main feature of the composition.

82 COAST SCENE NEAR GENOA

Pen and brown ink and brown and grey wash, over black chalk.
353 × 462 mm
Besançon, Musée des Beaux-Arts (D. 2850)

Provenance: P.-A. Pâris (see no. 79).

Literature: Paris, 1806, no. 119; Portalis, 1889, p. 295; *Le Paysage français de Poussin à Callot*, exh. Paris (Petit Palais), 1925, no. 421; Feuillet, 1926, pl. 27; Martine, 1927, pl. 15; *Le Dessin français dans les collections du* XVIII*è siècle*, exh. Paris (Galerie des Beaux-Arts), 1935, no. 258; Wilhelm, 1948, p. 33; *Le Musée de Besançon*, exh. Paris (Musée des Arts Decoratifs), 1957, no. 148; Cornillot, 1957, no. 38, repr.; Ananoff, iii, 1968, no. 1589.

Signed lower left, with the point of the brush in grey wash: *Fragonard*.

In the manuscript catalogue of his own collection which P.-A. Pâris drew up in 1806, he describes this view as having been drawn 'on the Genoese coast'. Presumably, therefore, it represents Aiguila, a place on the coast of Liguria where Fragonard and his friend and patron Bergeret de Grandcourt put in on their way to Italy in November 1773. In the drawings that Fragonard made on this second journey to Italy he abandoned red chalk for pen and brown wash, a medium in which he obtained effects of extraordinary transparency. The present drawing, like the two views of the Ponte San Stefano at Sestri, near Genoa, one of which is at Besançon (Cornillot, 1957, no. 45, repr.; Ananoff, iii, no. 1590) and the other, signed and dated 26 November 1773, at Lille (Ananoff, iii, no. 1589), is primarily a study of the effect of light, in which – as in some Chinese drawings – the contours of the forms are dissolved, while the figures are reduced to a few simple brush strokes.

83 AN ITALIAN GARDEN

Brown wash, with traces of underdrawing in black chalk.
347 × 463 mm
Paris, Musée du Petit Palais (Inv. Dutuit 965)

Provenance: H. Walferdin (sale, Paris, 12–16 April 1880, lot 237); E. and A. Dutuit (Lugt 709a), by whom bequeathed in 1902.

Literature: *Dessins de maîtres anciens*, exh. Paris (Ecole des Beaux-Arts) 1879, no. 580; Portalis, 1889, p. 316; Lapauze, 1907, no. 965; Lapauze, Gronkowski, Fauchier-Magnan, 1925, no. 1011; *Artistes français en Italie*, exh. Paris (Musée des Arts Decoratifs), 1934, no. 452; *Landscape in French Art*, exh. London (Royal Academy), 1949, no. 419, pl. 77; *Franse Landschap*, exh.

Amsterdam, 1951, no. 168, pl. 33; Fragonard, exh. Berne, 1954, no. 63; Ananoff, iv, 1970, no. 2151, fig. 585.

Signed on the step in the lower left corner, in brown ink: *Fragonard*.

This view of an Italian garden, probably an imaginary scene inspired by the Villa d'Este, is characteristic of Fragonard's style of drawing at the time of his second journey to Italy in 1773–4. Two very similar views at Besançon, of much the same size and identical in technique (Cornillot, 1957, nos. 46, 47, repr.: Ananoff, iv, nos. 2389 and 2252), were drawn in Rome in 1773 according to the manuscript catalogue of P.-A. Pâris, whose testimony has particular weight in view of the fact that he was there at that time in company with Fragonard and Bergeret de Grandcourt. These three drawings and the particularly characteristic *Umbrella-pines in the Villa Pamphili* in the Rijksmuseum (*Franse Tekenkunst van de 18de Eeuw*, exh. Amsterdam, 1974, no. 40, repr: Ananoff, iv, no. 2388, fig. 607) illustrate Fragonard's masterly handling of almost pure wash, over only a very slight underdrawing in black chalk. This was the technique that from then on he used for his landscape drawings. Comparison between the present drawing and the relatively realistic views of the Villa d'Este of thirteen years earlier (nos. 79, 80) shows the extent to which Fragonard had progressed towards romantic and poetic idealization in subjects of this kind. The figures strolling in the garden may suggest a *fête galante*, but they are subordinated – not to say overwhelmed – by their setting: the real interest of the drawing is in the rendering of the play of light and shadow in the foliage and the trees.

84 THE AVENUE
*

Drawn with the point of the brush in brown wash, over traces of black chalk underdrawing.
456 × 347 mm
Paris, Musée du Petit Palais (Inv. Dutuit 966)

Provenance: M. de Sireul (sale, Paris, 3 December 1781, lot 242); Saint (sale, Paris, 4 May 1846, lot 13); H. Walferdin (sale, Paris, 12–16 April 1880, lot 206); J. Gigoux (Lugt 1164: sale, Paris, 20–23 March 1882, lot 583, repr.); E. and A. Dutuit (Lugt 709a) by whom bequeathed in 1902.

Literature: *Dessins de maîtres anciens*, exh. Paris (Ecole des Beaux-Arts), 1879, no. 581; Portalis, 1889, pp. 293 f., repr. p. 40 (engraving by Greux); Lapauze, Gronkowski, Fauchier-Magnana, 1925, no. 1012, repr.; Martine, 1927, pl. 12; *Artistes français en Italie*, exh. Paris (Musée des Arts Decoratifs) 1934, no. 460; *Landscape in French Art*, exh. London (Royal Academy), 1949, no. 415; *Meisterwerke aus Frankreichs Museen*, exh. Amsterdam-Vienna, 1950, no. 125; *Franse Landschap*, exh. Amsterdam, 1951, no. 168, pl. 33; Ananoff, i, 1961, no. 327, fig. 120 and ii, 1963, fig. 365.

The exceptional quality of this drawing was already recognized in Fragonard's lifetime. It was described as 'superb' in the catalogue of the Sireul Sale of 1781. Fragonard executed several variations on this theme, particularly the drawing formerly in the S. Bardac and E. Esmond Collections (Ananoff, i, no. 328) and the painting now in the Metropolitan Museum. These views probably date from soon after his return in 1774 from his second Italian journey, and the scene is generally thought to have been in the garden of one of Bergeret de Grandcourt's country houses, either the château at Nointel, outside Paris, or at Négrepelisse, near Montauban.

HUBERT ROBERT

(Paris 1733 – Paris 1808)

Throughout his life Robert was blessed by exceptional good fortune. Born of a moderately well-off middle-class family and originally intended for the Church, he received an excellent education of which he took full advantage. His father had been *valet-de-chambre* to the father of the comte de Stainville, later duc de Choiseul and Louis xv's chief minister, who was appointed Ambassador to the Pope in 1754 at the moment when Robert, then a pupil in the studio of the sculptor René-Michel ('Michel-Ange') Slodtz, had failed in the competition for the Prix de Rome. Stainville invited him to travel to Rome as one of the ambassadorial party and arranged with Natoire, then Director of the French Academy, that he should be accommodated as a supernumerary *pensionnaire*. The beauty of Rome was a revelation to Robert and showed him at once where his true path lay; in the course of his eleven years there he made countless drawings of every picturesque aspect of the city and its surroundings, which served him for the rest of his life as an inexhaustible store of pictorial motifs. Of his older contemporaries, G. P. Panini, the leading specialist in Roman 'ruin pieces', had the greatest influence on him: Natoire early on described Robert's work as '*dans le genre de Panini*', and that this impression persisted is shown by the official record of his death in Paris more than half a century later, in which his name is given as '*Robert (Hubert), dit Robert des Ruines*'. In February 1759 Natoire reported to Marigny that Robert's influence was becoming predominant among the students at the Academy. These included Amand (q.v.) and also Fragonard (q.v.) who though two years older than Robert arrived in Rome more than two years later. The two became close friends and it was Robert's example that first turned Fragonard's mind to the possibilities of landscape. In 1760 they met their early patron, the Abbé de Saint-Non, who took Robert with him to Naples and Herculaneum and both of them – an experience of particular significance – to the Villa d'Este at Tivoli (see nos. 79, 80).

Robert's successful career continued after his return to Paris in 1765. In 1766 he received the exceptional compliment of admission on the same day to associate (*agréé*) and full membership of the Académie Royale de Peinture, presenting as his *morceau de réception* (Ecole des Beaux-Arts, Paris) a *capriccio* in the manner of Panini, in which he combined a number of Roman monuments including the Pantheon, the steps of the *Ripetta* and the Palazzo dei Conservatori (cf. nos. 89, 92). He continued tirelessly to make drawings – it was said that he could dash one off as quickly as he could write a letter – and his Parisian views and interior-scenes, quite apart from their intrinsic charm, are of interest as an accurate record of the appearance and daily life of the city in the years before the Revolution. Invited to St Petersburg by the Empress Catherine II, he refused but sent instead a large collection of his paintings (still in the Hermitage Museum). In 1778 he was put in charge of the planning of the royal gardens (in which capacity he redesigned some of the ornamental plantations at Versailles) and in 1784 of the royal collection of pictures. These links with the *ancien régime* led to his imprisonment during the Revolution, when his life was for a time in danger; but his good luck persisted and he survived until the fall of Robespierre in July 1794 put an end to the Terror. In 1795 he was appointed to the commission entrusted with the organization of the new Musée National, from which eventually developed the present Musée du Louvre.

Robert owed his success to a combination of qualities: great technical facility, an innate sense of proportion that enabled him to bring together Antiquity and the Picturesque without being either pedantic or sentimental; and an exact awareness of the taste of his public and the limitations of his own talent. Too exact an estimate of one's own limitations is in itself a limitation, and it cannot be denied that Robert was a more superficial artist than Fragonard. For Fragonard, the Villa d'Este drawings of 1760 were a point of departure, from which he went on to develop a style and technique of even greater subtlety and refinement; Robert, having hit on a successful formula, had the practical good sense to stick to it. But as a painter, especially in his smaller and sketchier canvases and when he is rendering something actually seen, he reveals an exquisite sense of colour and feeling for the physical manipulation of oil paint.

85 AN ANTIQUE TEMPLE SURROUNDED BY LATER BUILDINGS

Red chalk.
383 × 558 mm
Louvre, Cabinet des Dessins (RF 14,789)

Provenance: Comte de l'Espine; Princesse Louis de Croÿ, by whom presented in 1930.

Literature: *Oeuvres provenant des donations faites par Madame la Princesse Louis de Croÿ at Monsieur Louis Devillez*, exh. Paris (Orangerie), 1930–1, no. 42; *Monuments et sites d'Italie vus par les dessinateurs français de Callot à Degas*, exh. Paris (Louvre), 1958, no. 30.

Inscribed lower centre, in black chalk: *No 7*.

The style of this drawing suggests a date *c*. 1760, when Robert was in Rome; but in spite of such realistic details as the pergola in the foreground and the boarded-up colonnade the subject cannot be identified with any certainty. This may be a *capriccio* composed of elements suggested by such Roman buildings as the arch of the Portico of Octavia.

86 THE STEPS OF THE PALAZZO SENATORIO ON THE
* CAPITOL

Red chalk.
294 × 435 mm
Louvre, Cabinet des Dessins (RF 785)

Provenance: His de la Salle (Lugt 1332), by whom presented in 1878.

Literature: Gabillot, 1895, repr. opp. p. 104; Michel, 1906, p. 365; Nolhac-Loukomski, 1930, pl. 22; *Hubert Robert*, exh. Paris (Orangerie), 1933, no. 39; *L'Art français du XVIIIè siècle*, exh. Copenhagen, 1935, no. 490; *French Drawings from Fouquet to Gauguin*, exh. London (Arts Council), 1952, no. 138; *Dessins français, Miniatures du XVIIIè siècle*, exh. Paris (Louvre), 1954, no. 35; *L'Art et la pensée française du XVIIIè siècle*, exh. Vienna, 1966; no. 88, fig. 48; Beau, 1968, no. 21b; Cailleux, 1969, pl. 276, fig. 4; Cailleux, 1975, p. xiv, fig. 21 and note 66.

Dated lower centre, in red chalk: *1762*.

The date is sometimes read as 1760 and sometimes as 1762. The latter seems more likely, since this is the date clearly inscribed on some of the group of exactly similar views of the Capitol in the museum at Valence (Beau, 1968, nos. 19, 21–3: Mlle Beau reads the date on no. 19 as *1760*, but it could equally well be read as *1762*).

87 WASHERWOMEN IN THE RUINS OF THE TEMPLE OF
* SATURN

Red chalk.
453 × 352 mm
Louvre, Cabinet des Dessins (RF 14,792)

Provenance: Comte de l'Espine; Princesse Louis de Croÿ, by whom presented in 1930.

Literature: *Oeuvres provenant des donations faites par Madame la Princesse Louis de Croÿ et Monsieur Louis Devillez*, exh. Paris (Orangerie), 1930, no. 43; *Le Dessin français de Fouquet à Cezanne*, exh. Brussels-Rotterdam-Paris, 1949–50, no. 54; *Schönheit des 18 Jahrhunderts*, exh. Zurich, 1955, no. 280; *Monuments et sites d'Italie vus par les dessinateurs français de Callot à Degas*, exh. Paris (Louvre), 1958, no. 29.

The Temple of Saturn, in the north-west corner of the Forum, was a favourite subject with Hubert Robert. A view of the portico from the outside, dated 1762, is at Valence (Beau, 1968, no. 1, repr.), and the same date is inscribed on another view of the temple, seen from a different angle, in the Musée des Arts Decoratifs in Lyons (ibid., fig. 2e). The third drawing of the temple which Mlle Beau reproduces (ibid., fig. 2d) seems more likely to be by Vincent.

88 THE THEATRE OF MARCELLUS

Pen and brown wash with touches of white heightening.
158 × 227 mm
Louvre, Cabinet des Dessins (RF 30,621)

Provenance: probably either part of lot 346 or 353 in the artist's sale, Paris, 1809.

Literature: *Le Cabinet de l'amateur*, exh. Paris (Orangerie), 1956, no. 143.

This ancient Roman theatre, dating from the first century BC, was transformed into a fortified palace during the middle ages. It passed through the hands of various families, from the Fabi to the Savelli and from them in 1712 to the Orsini, whose name the palace still bears. Robert's view is looking northwards, towards the Piazza Montanara (now swept away by the construction of the wide Via del Teatro di Marcello, leading from the Piazza Venezia to the Piazza Bocca della Verità) and the church of S. Maria in Campitelli, the cupola of which is visible in the background (cf. the eighteenth-century views by Piranesi, Vasi and others, reproduced in Marabottini-Origo-Crea, *Theatrum Marcelli: 'El Quliseo de' Savelli'*, Rome, 1973). Comparison with these views shows that Robert has exaggerated the scale of the houses on either side, to make his composition more dramatic.

**89 THE SPANISH STEPS WITH THE CHURCH OF S.
* TRINITA DEI MONTI AND THE VILLA MEDICI**

Pen and brown ink and brown and grey wash.
123 × 220 mm
Louvre, Cabinet des Dessins (RF 30,591)

Provenance: as for no. 88.

Literature: Monuments et sites d'Italie vus par les dessinateurs français de Callot à Degas, exh. Paris (Louvre), 1958, no. 32; *Vingt ans d'acquisitions au Musée du Louvre*, 1947–67, exh. Paris (Orangerie), 1967–8, no. 510.

The Spanish Steps were built in 1721–5 and ascend from the Piazza di Spagna to the southern end of the Pincian Hill, immediately opposite the church and convent of S. Trinità dei Monti. The drawing is not a faithful representation of the view: the scale and relative position of the steps and the church and the Villa Medici on the extreme left have been slightly distorted in order to produce a monumental composition which might almost be called a *capriccio*.

90 A FESTIVAL AT NIGHT IN THE PIAZZA ST PIETRO

Pen and brown wash over black chalk.
127 × 193 mm
Louvre, Cabinet des Dessins (RF 30,605)

Provenance: as for no. 88.

The Piazza San Pietro was frequently the setting for festivals and processions. The presence of the tabernacle at the end of one arm of the colonnade suggests that this drawing may represent one of the ceremonies of the Feast of Corpus Christi.

91 THE COURTYARD OF A ROMAN PALACE

Pen and brown wash over black chalk.
170 × 225 mm
Louvre, Cabinet des Dessins (RF 30,596)

Provenance: as for no. 88.

**92 'CAPRICCIO' OF ROMAN BUILDINGS
***

Red chalk.
392 × 532 mm
Louvre, Cabinet des Dessins (RF 14,794) .

Provenance: Comte de l'Espine; Princesse Louis de Croÿ, by whom presented in 1930.

Literature: Leclerc, 1913, p. 88; *Oeuvres provenant des donations faites par Madame la Princesse Louis de Croÿ et Monsieur Louis Devillez*, exh. Paris (Orangerie), 1930–1, no. 46; *Dessins français du Musée du Louvre*, exh. Berne, 1948, no. 60; *Amis et contemporains de P.-J. Mariette*, exh. Paris (Louvre), 1967, no. 92, pl. xvi; Bacou, 1971, p. 84, pl. xxii.

This mélange of Roman monuments includes a fountain from the garden of the Villa Albani (another drawing of which by Robert is also in the Louvre, RF 14,784), the Arch of Titus, and the Pyramid of Cestius. The palace on the left was possibly inspired by the loggia on the garden façade of the Villa Medici. Robert was continually harking back to the repertoire of pictorial motifs which he had formed in Rome: the same assortment of elements occurs, for example, in his *Villa Medici* (H. de Wendel Coll., Paris) and in one of a pair of gouaches, signed and dated 1782, formerly in Lord Brownlow's collection (sale, Sotheby's, 29 June 1926, lot 15b).

An offset of the present drawing, at Besançon (Feuillet, 1926, no. 60), probably served as basis for a painting by Robert, dated 1775, composed in reverse of the same elements except for the Arch of Titus and the Pyramid (Robert-Jones, 1963, fig. 21).

**93 TWO LADIES SKETCHING A HEAP OF FRAGMENTS
* OF ANTIQUE SCULPTURE**

Pen and black ink and watercolour.
750 × 980 mm
Louvre, Cabinet des Dessins (RF 21,695)
Provenance: Comtesse d'Angiviller (given as her property in the catalogue of the Salon of 1787); anon. sale, Paris, Palais Galliera, 11 December 1961, lot 11, repr.; acquired by the Louvre in 1965.

Literature: Salon of 1787, no. 52; *Amis et contemporains de P.-J. Mariette*, exh. Paris (Louvre), 1967, no. 94; *Vingt ans d'acquisitions au Musée du Louvre*, exh. Paris (Orangerie), 1967–8, no. 514, repr.; *Dessins français de 1750 à 1825: Le Néo-Classicisme*, exh. Paris (Louvre), 1972, no. 17.

Signed and dated in pen, lower centre: *H. Robert 1786.*

Robert has provided three pieces of sculpture as subjects for this pair of elegant young ladies: the damaged colossal statue of a Dacian Captive, in the Vatican; part of the relief of the Triumph of Titus from the interior of the Arch of Titus in the Forum; and the same standing statue of Minerva that occurs in his painting of the *Ruined Portico*, dated 1793, in the

Louvre. These reminiscences of Rome are rendered in watercolour, a technique that Robert increasingly used towards the end of the century.

94 A COUNTRY-HOUSE IN TOURAINE

Red chalk.

304 × 455 mm

Louvre, Cabinet des Dessins (RF 14,790)

Provenance: Comte de l'Espine; Princesse Louis de Croÿ, by whom presented in 1930.

Literature: *Oeuvres provenant des donations faites par Madame la Princesse Louis de Croÿ et Monsieur Louis Devillez*, exh. Paris (Orangerie), 1930–1, no. 48.

The same house occurs in one of the four overdoor paintings commissioned in 1769 from J.-L. Houel (q.v.) by the duc de Choiseul for his château at Chanteloup, and now in the museum at Tours (Lossky, 1962, nos. 45–7). Three of the four, including the one in question, are similar in size and apparently *en suite*, and represent scenes in the valley of the Loire near Chanteloup. (The house is described in the old catalogues of the Tours Museum as being at Saint-Ouen-les-Vignes, but Lossky does not accept this identification.)

It is not surprising that Robert should have worked in the neighbourhood of Chanteloup: his father and mother had been servants to the duc de Choiseul's parents, and it was through the good offices of Choiseul himself that he was able to go to Rome in 1754. Choiseul retired to Chanteloup after his fall from power in 1770 and died there in 1785. Two offsets of drawings of park-scenes at Besançon (Cornillot, 1957, nos. 154–5; the latter better repr. Feuillet, 1926, pl. li) are both inscribed, in the hand of Robert's friend the collector P.-A. Pâris, *Robert à Chanteloup*. The lost original of Cornillot 155 was inscribed *janvier 1790*. If this date is to be accepted as authentic (it may perhaps be questioned whether the trees would still have been in full leaf as late as January) Robert must have visited Chanteloup even after Choiseul's death, when his heirs had sold the château. The original of the other offset, incorrectly identified as a view in the Villa Negroni in Rome, is in the museum at Valenciennes.

95 THE GARDENS OF THE TUILERIES FROM THE PLACE LOUIS XV

Red chalk.

320 × 450 mm

Besançon, Musée des Beaux-Arts (D. 2979)

Provenance: P.-A. Pâris (see no. 79).

Literature: Besançon *Inventaire*, 1886, p. 255; Leclère, 1913, p. 53; *Le Paysage français de Poussin à Corot*, exh. Paris (Petit Palais), 1925, no. 668; Feuillet, 1926, pl. lxvii; Chudant, 1929, no. 214; Sentenac, 1929, pl. 46; *Chefs d'oeuvre de l'art français des Musées de Province*, exh. Paris (Musée Carnavalet), 1933, no. 267; *Hubert Robert*,

exh. Paris (Orangerie), 1933, no. 187; *Le dessin français de Fouquet à Cézanne*, exh. Brussels-Rotterdam-Paris, 1949–50, no. 95, pl. 44; *Het Franse Landschap*, exh. Amsterdam, 1951, no. 211; Cornillot, 1957, no. 153 (repr.).

Signed in chalk, lower left: *Robert f.*

A view of the west end of the Tuileries Gardens from the Place Louis XV (now Place de la Concorde), looking across the swivel-bridge (*pont tournant*) which then spanned the sunk fence. The sculpture on the entrance pier is the equestrian figure of *Fame* by Antoine Coysevox which with its counterpart, *Mercury*, was moved from Marly in 1719. They were replaced there in 1745 by the pair of *Horses with grooms* (the 'Chevaux de Marly'), the work of Nicolas and Guillaume Coustou, which in their turn were moved to the Place de la Concorde in 1795 and placed on the opposite side, flanking the end of the Champs-Elysées. A painting by J.-B. Le Prince in the Besançon Museum is of the same view but seen from further back so that the whole entrance to the gardens is included as well as Bouchardon's equestrian statue of Louis XV which stood with the head pointing towards the Tuileries (repr. *Dictionnaire de Paris*, Paris (Larousse), 1964, p. 146).

There seems to be no particular reason why Robert should have made this drawing in connection with his proposed painting of the firework display celebrating the marriage of the Dauphin (later Louis XVI) and the Archduchess Marie Antoinette in 1770, as Réau (1927, p. 210) has suggested.

A drawing of the same view, slightly smaller in size, was in the M. Paulme Sale in 1929 (Paris, Galerie Georges Petit, 14 May, lot 224, repr.). Another view of the Place Louis XV in the same collection, seen from the north-west corner looking north-east and showing the two buildings by Gabriel on either side of the present Rue Royale, was bought by the Musée Carnavalet. Another version is at Valence (Beau, 1968, no. 84).

JEAN-BAPTISTE LE PRINCE

(Metz 1734 – St Denis du Port 1781)

Coming to Paris as a protégé of the Governor of Lorraine, the Maréchal de Belle-Isle, Le Prince entered the studio of Boucher whose influence is reflected in his earliest landscapes (e.g. the series of six ovals engraved by Saint-Non in his *Recueil de Griffonis*). In 1754 he was in Italy, and from that period date some red chalk drawings of ruins (e.g. sale, Paris, Palais Galliera, 1960, 14 December, lot 60, pl. xxxv; sale, Versailles, 1911, 3 December, lot 44, repr.).

From Italy he went to Holland and from there, in 1757, to Russia. Such paintings as *The Fisherman* (Pushkin Museum, Moscow), *River landscape* (Orléans) and *The Beggar* (Rey Sale, Paris, 1901, 8 May, lot 102) reveal an understanding of Dutch seventeenth-century landscape and a vigorous technique both unusual in French art of that period. In Russia, where he remained until 1763, he carried out a number of decorative paintings, mostly over-doors, ceilings etc. (now destroyed) in the Winter Palace for Catherine II and developed a genuine interest in the country and its people and customs. The painting of *The Russian Christening* (Louvre) which he presented to the Académie Royale de Peinture in 1765 as his *morceau de réception* was singled out for praise by Diderot and launched a short-lived vogue for a new kind of exoticism. In 1767 he designed six cartoons for a popular series of Beauvais tapestries, *Les Jeux russes*; but his 'russerie' soon became a mere pretext for subjects in unusual fancy dress.

In 1775 Le Prince settled in the country not far from Paris, and spent the last years of his life in a closer study of nature. He is now chiefly remembered as one of the pioneers (if not necessarily the inventor, as is sometimes claimed) of the aquatint process of engraving. His earliest prints in this process are dated 1768. He used it to reproduce his own drawings, especially those of Russian subjects, costumes, etc.

96 A FISHING-BOAT ON A RIVER, WITH A CASTLE IN THE BACKGROUND

Pen and black ink and brown wash.
338 × 217 mm
Louvre, Cabinet des Dessins (30,632)

Literature: Guiffrey-Marcel, ix, no. 9141, repr.

The composition of an aquatint by Le Prince entitled *Les Laveuses* (Jules Hédou, *Jean Le Prince et son oeuvre*, Paris, 1879, no. 148) is identical in style and format and is almost exactly the same size. This drawing is no doubt a preliminary study for the companion print, *Les Pêcheurs* (Hédou, no. 163). Both prints are dated 1771. So far as it goes, Hédou's description of *Les Pêcheurs* corresponds exactly with the drawing, but there is no impression of it either in the British Museum or in the Cabinet des Estampes of the Bibliothèque Nationale.

97 A FIELD BY A RIVER, WITH A PLOUGH DRAWN BY
* THREE HORSES

Pen and brown wash over black chalk.
230 × 295 mm
Louvre, Cabinet des Dessins (30,624)

Literature: Guiffrey-Marcel, ix, no. 9143.

Signed and dated in pen, lower right: *Le Prince 1777*.

The landscape setting looks like part of the Ile-de-France or, perhaps more likely, the Brie district to the south-east of Paris where Le Prince was living from 1775 to 1781; but he has been unable to resist the temptation of putting Russian-style harness on his three-horse tandem. Much the same observation was made by Dupont de Nemours in the account of the Salon of 1777 which he sent to the Margravine of Baden: 'until this year all M. Le Prince's pictures, whatever their subject, have been Russian; just as almost all Casanova's have been German' (*Archives de l'art français*, 1908, p. 57), and also by Bachaumont: 'This year, Le Prince has been the particular attraction. He no longer takes us to Russia, but paints delightful places near Paris which one can easily recognize. It is annoying now and then to come across a vestige of his former subject-matter in the shape of something obviously Russian' (*Lettres sur les peintures, sculptures et gravures des Mrs de l'Académie royale exposées au Sallon du Louvre*, London, 1780, pp. 257 f.).

LOUIS-NICOLAS DE LESPINASSE

(Pouilly 1734 – Pouilly 1808)

Lespinasse came from a family of the provincial nobility in the neighbourhood of Nevers and might have been classed as an amateur if he had not been elected to the Académie Royale de Peinture in 1787 as *peintre de paysages et de vues perspectives à la gouache*. His *morceau de réception* was the panoramic view of Paris, no. 99 in the present exhibition. He exhibited at the Salon from 1787 to 1801, and in 1801 published a treatise on perspective. His well-known series of views of Paris combine purity of line and freshness of colour with an extraordinarily exact sense of topographical and atmospherical accuracy. He had a particular feeling for the transformation brought about by the change in the light at different times of day, and often inscribed on his drawings the hour when they were made. On one of the two views of Paris exhibited, which are among the masterpieces of late-eighteenth-century Parisian topographical drawing, he has noted that 'the lighting of this picture is that of the hour between 11 o'clock and midday'.

98 THE PORT ST PAUL IN PARIS

* Pen and brown ink with watercolour and bodycolour.
290 × 625 mm
Paris, Musée Carnavalet (D. 5329)

Literature: Bourin, 1910, pp. 26 f.; M. Roux, *Catalogue des estampes de la Bibliothèque Nationale: Fonds Français*, iii, Paris, 1933, no. 19; *Trois siècles de dessin parisien*, exh. Paris (Musée Carnavalet) 1946, no. 216; *Dessins parisiens du XVIIIè siècle*, exh. Paris (Musée Carnavalet) 1972, repr. on cover.

Signed and dated in pen, lower left: *d. L. 1782*.

The wharf of St Paul, which Lespinasse has represented at a moment of activity caused by the arrival of a passenger-boat, was on the left bank of the Seine, downstream from the Quai des Celestins. The houses of the *quai*, extending from the end of the rue St Paul to the Arsenal, can be seen on the left in the drawing, and in the distance the buildings and church of the Celestine convent from which the *quai* takes its name. On the right is the Ile St-Louis and in the centre, covered with enormous piles of wood, the Ile Louviers, connected with the right bank by the pont de Grammont. This bridge crosses a branch of the Seine which has since been filled in and has become the Boulevard Morland.

99 PANORAMIC VIEW OF PARIS LOOKING NORTH

* Pen and brown ink with watercolour and bodycolour.
480 × 991 mm
Paris, Musée Carnavalet (D. 5367)

Provenance: transferred from the Louvre in 1934.

Literature: Salon de 1787, no. 155; Bonnardot, 1837, p. 39; Bouzin, 1910, p. 27 etc.; Guiffrey-Marcel, ix, no. 9150, repr.; *Rétif de la Bretonne*, exh. Paris (Musée

Carnavalet) 1934, no. 93; *Trois siècles de dessin parisien*, exh. Paris (Musée Carnavalet) 1946, no. 212; *Dessins parisiens du XVIIIè siècle*, exh. Paris (Musée Carnavalet), 1972, no. 61.

Inscribed on the mount in pen, presumably by the draughtsman:

Vue intérieure de Paris, prise du Belveder de la maison de M. Fournel, rue des Boulangers, Fossés Saint-Victor, c'est-à-dire à deux cents pieds du niveau de la rivière de Seine. Ainsi l'oeil embrasse un horizon très étendu qui présente dans ses détails le Dôme de l'Hopital général, Saint Maur, Bercy, Vincennes, Romainville, Ménilmontant, Saint-Denis, Montmartre, les Buttes de Sanois et se termine vers l'Etoile; se portant ensuite sur la Capitale, il voit la Seine formant un col de Cygne et qui semble la partager; il reconnoît les principaux Edifices Sacrés, tels que Notre-Dame, la Ste.-Chapelle, &c. &c. les Edifices Royaux tels que le Jardin du Roi, l'Arsenal, la Bastille etc., comme aussi les Richesses et le Commerce des Ports St. Bernard, St. Paul et Delarapée. Au pied du Belveder d'où l'on a pris cette vue on distinguera sans doute avec plaisir entr'autres objets le Jardin et la Maison de repos que le célèbre LE BRUN 1er peintre de Louis XIV, s'etoit fait construire non loin des Gobelins qu'il occupoit et diregoit. L'heure du jour dont ce tableau est éclairé est celle entre onze heures et midi. Dessinée d'après nature en 1786, par M. de Lespinasse, Ch.er de St. Louis.

This drawing was the diploma piece presented by Lespinasse to the Royal Academy of Painting on his election on 30 June 1787. The belvedere from which he drew this view and two years later the similar panorama in the other direction (no. 100) still exists on the roof of no. 30 rue des Boulangers. The Hôtel Le Brun in the left foreground of the drawing, now no. 49 rue du Cardinal-Lemoine, was not built for the painter Charles Le Brun (1619–90) as Lespinasse states in the inscription, but in 1700 for his nephew, to the design of the architect Germain Boffrand. Among the buildings shown which were demolished at the beginning of the nineteenth century are the churches of the Abbey of St Victor (on the right) and of the Bernardine convent near Notre Dame.

100 PANORAMIC VIEW OF PARIS LOOKING SOUTH

Pen and brown ink with watercolour and bodycolour.
517 × 1000 mm
Paris, Musée Carnavalet (D. 5366)

Provenance: transferred from the Louvre in 1934.

Literature: Bourin, 1910, pp. 25 etc.; Guiffrey-Marcel, ix, no. 9151; *Rétif de la Bretonne*, exh. Paris (Musée Carnavalet) 1934, no. 92; *Trois siècles de dessin parisien*, exh. Paris (Musée Carnavalet), 1946, no. 213; *Dessins parisiens du* XVIIIè *siècle*, exh. Paris (Musée Carnavalet) 1972, no. 62.

Signed and dated in pen, on one of the chimney-stacks on the left: *Lespinasse 1788*. Inscribed on the mount in pen, presumably by the draughtsman: *Vüe interieure de Paris prise du Belveder de M!. Fornelle rue des Boulangers Saint Victor. Cette Vüe présente pour Objets principaux, l'ancienne et la N.lle S.te Genevieve, S! Etienne Dumont, les Jardins & Maisons des D.es Anglaises, des Doctrinaires, des Augustines, partie du f.g. S! Marceau, les N.eaux Boulevards, Bicêtre, &c.*

A companion to no. 99 (q.v.). On the right can be seen Soufflot's new church of St Geneviève, then under construction. It was completed in 1790 and in the following year, by decree of the Constituent Assembly, was transformed into the Pantheon.

JEAN-PIERRE HOUEL

(Rouen 1735 – Paris 1813)

After studying at the academy in Rouen founded by J.-B. Descamps (best known as the author of *Les vies des peintres flamands, allemands et hollandais*) and after a period of apprenticeship to an architect, Houel decided to take up engraving and in 1755 began to work in Paris under Le Bas and Le Mire, two of the leading engravers of the day. His engravings of Boucher's *Livre de paysages* (1759) and his earliest paintings, in which he benefited from the advice of Francesco Casanova, show that he already had a leaning towards landscape. Introduced into the artistic world by his patron Blondel de Azincourt, son of the well-known collector Blondel de Gagny, he received a commission from the duc de Choiseul for a set of four landscape over-doors for his château at Chanteloup (see no. 94). These paintings, dated 1769 and now in the museum at Tours, reveal the influence of the Dutch seventeenth-century landscape which then appealed particularly to French taste. In 1769 he went to Rome, where the influence of Choiseul had procured for him the privilege of living at the French Academy, and later in the same year to Naples. In the following year he returned to Naples and from there made his first visit to Sicily.

On his return to Paris in 1772 he conceived the idea of publishing a book on Sicily. Thanks to Watelet's intervention on his behalf with the comte d'Angiviller, the Superintendent of the King's buildings and works of art, he was able to spend from 1776 to 1779 travelling there. His book, *Voyage pittoresque des isles de Sicile, de Lipari et de Malte*, illustrated with aquatints which he engraved himself after his own drawings, was published between 1783 and 1787.

Houel is today mainly remembered for the series of views of Sicily in the Louvre. These drawings combine a strongly realistic, even scientific, approach to their subject with a vein of genuinely poetic feeling, an acute sensitivity to effects of light and atmosphere, and an unusually subtle sense of colour. In some ways they anticipate later developments: in a drawing like no. 106, for example, those features of Dutch seventeenth-century landscape – the open foreground and the low horizon with its suggestion of limitless space – are emphasized that were to be taken up by the landscape draughtsmen of the Romantic period. The tradition of landscape painting in watercolour (as opposed to making tinted drawings) was less deeply rooted in France in the eighteenth century than it was in Holland and England, so that Houel's apparently spontaneous mastery of the medium as early as the 1770's is something of a phenomenon. His closest French parallel is his slightly younger contemporary Louis-Gabriel Moreau l'aîné (1740–1806); but Houel's drawings, unlike Moreau's, also challenge comparison with those of the English watercolourists active in Italy in the 1770's – Francis Towne, 'Warwick' Smith and John Robert Cozens – and with those of their contemporaries, the Swiss draughtsman Louis Ducros and the German Philipp Hackert, both often cited as important influences on the development of the English watercolour school. But there is no evidence that Houel ever came into contact with any of these artists; certainly nothing about his drawings suggests any direct influence.

Views of Sicily

In the 1770's the Kingdom of Sicily suddenly became a centre of interest. The Scottish traveller Patrick Brydone went there in 1770 and in 1773 published his *Tour through Sicily and Malta*, which was followed in 1783–5 by Henry Swinburne's *Travels in the Two Sicilies in the years 1777, 1778, 1779 and 1780*. Between 1781 and 1786 appeared the five volumes of the Abbé de Saint

Non's *Voyage pittoresque ou description des royaumes de Naples et de Sicile*, and between 1783 and 1787 the four volumes of Houel's *Voyage pittoresque des Isles de Sicile, de Lipari et de Malte*. Though, as reading matter the books by the two British travellers are no less interesting than those by their French counterparts, these wholly eclipse them in the magnificence of their production and their wealth of illustration. Saint Non's *Voyage pittoresque* was lavishly embellished with engravings, mostly after Jean-Louis Desprez and Claude-Louis Chatelet; while Houel illustrated his own text with no fewer than two hundred and sixty-four aquatints, etched by himself, which reproduce drawings made by him in the course of his travels between 1776 and 1779. Forty-six of these drawings were selected in 1780 for the Museum of Paintings at Versailles and are now in the Cabinet de Dessins of the Louvre (27147–92: Guiffrey-Marcel, vi, nos. 4831–76). They are signed by Houel and also by J.-B. Pierre, Painter in Ordinary to the King, and C.-N. Cochin, Keeper of the Royal Collection of Drawings. Nine of them are included in the present exhibition (nos. 102–10). Comparison with the corresponding plates in the *Voyage pittoresque* shows that Houel in many cases enlivened his illustrations by the addition of figures.

Houel financed his publication by selling five hundred of his watercolours to the Empress Catherine II of Russia. Two hundred and sixty are still in the Hermitage in Leningrad (Oglov and Roche, 1925, pp. 577–86).

101 LAKE AVERNUS
*

Watercolour and bodycolour.
265 × 435 mm
Louvre, Cabinet des Dessins (27,146)

Provenance: marquis d'Havrincourt; Revolutionary confiscation.

Literature: Guiffrey-Marcel. vi, no. 4880; *Amis et contemporains de Mariette*, exh. Paris, 1967, no. 95

Signed and dated in pen, lower left: *J. Hoüel f. 1769*.

Houel had hardly arrived in Rome in June 1769 when he was instructed by Natoire, then Director of the French Academy there, to accompany the young chevalier (later marquis) d'Havrincourt to Naples. The present drawing was made during this first visit to the south of Italy which was to have so decisive an effect on Houel's future (see his *Travel Notes* in Vlöberg, 1930, pp. 35–40). In the Revolution the marquis d'Havrincourt fled the country. The 'three drawings by Houel representing views of sea-shores and ruins' included in the list of property confiscated from his house in Paris (Furcy-Raynaud, 1911, p. 53), are the present drawing and two panoramic views of the Gulf of Naples now also in the Louvre (27,145 and 27,145 bis; Guiffrey-Marcel, vi, nos. 4877–8).

Among other works by Houel that predate the series of drawings made for the *Voyage pittoresque* may be mentioned a black chalk drawing of a ruined courtyard at Capo di Monte, dated 1770, also in the Louvre (27,143; Guiffrey-Marcel, no. 4879). In the same year Houel sent Mariette 'an example of his way of painting in gouache which has been praised by everyone to whom I have shown it' (*Abecedario*, ii, p. 386).

102 THE REMAINS OF THE BRIDGE AT LILYBAEUM

Watercolour and bodycolour over black chalk.
335 × 520 mm
Louvre, Cabinet des Dessins (27,181)

Literature: Guiffrey-Marcel, vi, no. 4856.

Signed in pen, lower left: *J. Hoüel f.*; lower right, the signature of *Pierre* and *Cochin*. Inscribed on the mount in ink: *Vue du focé qui entourait l'antique ville de Lilibée où Etait une Entrée de cette ville, dont on voit l'endroit où Etait le pont pour cette Entrée. Plan. gravée 10,*; and in black chalk: *35. Vue des restes du Port antique de Lilybée.*

Engraved, with the addition of figures, in vol. i. of the *Voyage pittoresque*, pl. 10, with the title *Vue du Port antique de Lilibée*. The drawing is considerably larger than most of the rest of the series.

The ancient city of Lilybaeum occupied the site of the modern city of Marsala, on Cape Boeo, the westernmost part of Sicily. Houel seems to be looking at the remains of its fortifications with the eye of an archaeologist; but the eye of the artist is no less evident in his treatment of the subject – in the suppression of obviously picturesque elements, the vigorous rendering of the various tones of the ground and the foliage, and the breadth of the handling.

103 THE ISLAND OF VOLCANO

Watercolour and bodycolour over black chalk.
268 × 428 mm
Louvre, Cabinet des Dessins (27,192)

Literature: Guiffrey-Marcel, vi, no. 4876.

Signed in pen lower left: *Hoüel f. 26*; lower right, the signature of *Pierre* and *Cochin*. Inscribed on the mount, in ink: *Vue d'une des îles de Lipari apellé Volcano, c'est un volcan ralenti dont la bouche s'est close et qui ne jette que de la fumée par plusieurs endroits, il a des laves et des scories très différents des autres volcans et d'autres particularités très curieuses, planche gravée 62*; and in black chalk: *46 Première vue générale de l'Ile de Volcano, prise au midi de Lipari.*

Engraved in vol. i of the *Voyage pittoresque*, pl. 62, with the title *Première vue generale de l'Ile de Volcano, prise au midi de Lipari.* The sub-title given in the text, *Manière dont on laboure et dont on sème a Lipari*, shows Houel's interest not only in the landscape but also in the life and customs of the country: 'in the foreground of this print' he writes 'I have introduced peasants, and some animals in a field, exactly like those that I saw there while I was engaged in drawing'.

104 THE CRATER OF STROMBOLI

Watercolour and bodycolour over black chalk.
298 × 445 mm
Louvre, Cabinet des Dessins (27,172)

Literature: Guiffrey-Marcel, vi, no. 4866; Vloberg, p. 173, pl. lviii.

Signed in pen, lower left: *Hoüel f. 27*; lower right, the signatures of *Pierre* and *Cochin*. Inscribed on the mount in ink: *Vue de la bouche* [*de Stromboli* added in black chalk] *et du sommet de Stromboli, Volcan situé en plaine mer à 15 lieues ou environs de l'italie et de la Sicile; la multiplicité de poins rouge que l'on voit rassemblés marques les jets de pierres dans l'état de charbons ardens jette ce volcan, j'en ai vu constamment quatre par heure de cette éspece, ils sont accompagnes d'un bruit effrayant – Plan, grav. 72*; and in black chalk: STRA 26.

Engraved in vol. i of the *Voyage pittoresque*, pl. 72, with the title *Vue de la bouche de Stromboli*. The artist gives a lively account of his impression of the scene on pp. 133–5: 'The way there prepared us for what we were to see; ashes, black, red and yellow cinders, fragments of lava and volcanic dust of all colours, warned us that we were approaching an infernal region . . . I had been surveying the magnificent spectacle for ten or twelve minutes when a sudden ear-splitting noise made me tremble. As I watched, a mass of red-hot stones of all shapes and sizes came pouring from the depths of the abyss, increasing in size until it was like a great plume of feathers thirty yards high . . . During all these explosions I continued with my drawing, though my ears were unable to accustom themselves to the extraordinary and terrifying noise that accompanied each discharge of stones; but the horror that I felt in this frightful place was not unmixed with pleasure at the beauty of the fiery sight'.

105 ETNA FROM OUTSIDE CATANIA

Watercolour and bodycolour, over black chalk.
305 × 482 mm

Louvre, Cabinet des Dessins (27,190)

Literature: Guiffrey-Marcel, vi, no. 4853, repr.; Ouglov and Roche, p. 577; Vlöberg, 1930, pp. 161 f., pl. li.

Signed in pen, lower left: *J. Hoüel f.*; lower right, the signatures of *Pierre* and *Cochin*. Inscribed on the mount in ink: *6, Vue generale de l'etna et d'un des faubourgs de Catania, prise à la place nommé porta diaci* [corrected in black chalk to: *porta d'Aci*] *entre les Capucins à gauche et l'hopital à droitte – planche gravée 151*; and in black chalk: *44.*

Engraved in vol. ii of the *Voyage pittoresque*, pl. 151, on which this view is used as the setting for the subject described in the title of the plate: *La Fête de la moisson passant dans la place de Porto d'Aci.* The occasion is described on pp. 17 f. of the same volume. The illustrations in Saint-Non's *Voyage pittoresque* include a view of Etna from the Capuchin Convent at Catania, after a drawing by Chatelet (vol. iv, pl. 24).

106 THE ROMAN AMPHITHEATRE AT SYRACUSE
*
Watercolour and bodycolour, over black chalk.
302 × 483 mm
Louvre, Cabinet des Dessins (27,186)

Literature: Guiffrey-Marcel, vi, no. 4872.

Signed in pen, lower left: *J. Hoüel f. 11e*; lower right, the signatures of *Pierre* and *Cochin*. Inscribed on the mount in ink: *40, Vue du petit amphithéatre de Siracuse lequel étoit à plus de moitié de sa hauteur sculpté dans la roche vive, l'arrène, les vomitoires, les gradins ou sièges et une grande gallerie qui en faisat le tour avec ses chambres adjacentes. Le reste des gradins etaient formés avec de la massonerie et un mastic qui subsiste encore aujourduy en partie, lequel imite parfaitement le pierre quant à la couleur et la dureté*; and in black chalk: *Vue g[énéra]le de l'amphitheatre avec la ville et le port de Siracuse.*

Engraved in vol. iii of the *Voyage pittoresque*, pl. 185, with the title *Vue générale de l'amphitheatre avec la ville et le port de Siracuse*. Some figures have been added in the engraving, notably a peasant in the foreground with a cow and a goat. It is clear from the text that Houel himself made excavations on this site. In the drawing, the simplicity of the subject – a few Antique fragments scarcely visible in a bare landscape – and the emphasis on the treatment of light, challenge comparison with the most austere and unadorned landscapes of Moreau l'ainé; while the subtlety of the colour foreshadows some of the late watercolours of Granet.

107 THE GREEK THEATRE AT SYRACUSE
*
Watercolour and bodycolour over black chalk.
285 × 483 mm
Louvre, Cabinet des Dessins (27,180)

Literature: Guiffrey-Marcel, vi, no. 4871; Vloberg, p. 169, pl. lv.

Signed in pen, lower left: *J. Hoüel f. 16*; lower right, the signatures of *Pierre* and *Cochin*. Inscribed on the mount, in ink: *Vue de l'intérieur du Théâtre di Siracuse où l'on voit les gradins lesquels étoient taillés dans la roche – planche gravée 188*; and in black chalk: *34, Vue particulière du Théatre de Syracuse*.

Engraved, with the addition of figures, in vol. iii of the *Voyage pittoresque*, pl. 188, with the title *Vue particulière du Théâtre de Syracuse*. In the text (pp. 88f.) Houel describes how he and his friend the Cavaliere Saverio Lendinola excavated the soil which had buried most of the tiers of seats in the hope of discovering inscriptions. A *Vue générale du Theatre de Syracuse* is on plate 187 of Houel's *Voyage pittoresque* and an *Elévation géométrale du Théatre* on plate 189; an engraving of the Theatre after Desprez is one of the illustrations in Saint-Non's *Voyage pittoresque* (vol. v, pl. 112).

108 THE RUINS OF THE TEMPLE OF HERCULES AT
* AGRIGENTUM
Watercolour and bodycolour, over black chalk.
298 × 454 mm
Louvre, Cabinet des Dessins (27,173)
Literature: Guiffrey-Marcel, no. 4838.

Signed in pen, lower left: *J. Hoüel f.*; lower right, the signatures of *Pierre* and *Cochin*. Inscribed on the mount in ink: *21 Reste du Temple d'Hercule d'Agrigente – planche gravée 225*; and in black chalk: AGRI, 27 . . .

Engraved, with the addition of figures, in vol. iv of the *Voyage pittoresque*, pl. 225, with the title *Débris du Temple d'Hercule*. The temple stood on top of a cliff on the very edge of the site of the ancient city of Agrigentum. When Houel drew it, the only part left standing was a single doric column protruding from a confused heap of stones, but in 1924 seven of the fallen columns were re-erected. His description of this desolate scene has already a certain romantic flavour: 'Les débris qui en restent sont épars; le temps les a presque tous dévorés; des terres se sont amassées entre eux et en recouvrent une partie; des arbres et de broussailles s'élèvent au dessus de toutes parts'. The same site was drawn by Desprez to illustrate Saint-Non's *Voyage pittoresque* (vol. iv, pl. 89).

109 THE 'TOMB OF THERON' AT AGRIGENTUM
*
Watercolour and bodycolour with touches of pen and brown ink.
290 × 421 mm
Louvre, Cabinet des Dessins (27,164)
Literature: Guiffrey-Marcel, vi, no. 4841.

Signed in pen, lower left: *J. Hoüel f.*; lower right, the signatures of *Pierre* and *Cochin*. Inscribed on the mount in ink: *Tombeau antique que l'on croit être celui de Heron Tiran d'agrigente – planche 226*; and in black chalk: AGRI 18.

Engraved, with the addition of figures of shepherds with sheep and goats, in vol. iv of the *Voyage pittoresque*, pl. 226, with the title *Tombeau antique que l'on croit être celui de Théron, Tiran d'Agrigente*. On the hill to the left can be seen the ruins of the Temple of Hercules (see no. 108). The building traditionally identified as the tomb of Theron, tyrant of Agrigentum in the fifth century BC, is in reality a *heroon* or local shrine dating from the Roman occupation some two or three hundred years later. The building was also drawn by Desprez to illustrate Saint-Non's *Voyage pittoresque* (vol. iv, pl. 88).

110 THE 'ORATORY OF PHALARIS' AT AGRIGENTUM
* Watercolour and bodycolour, with touches of pen and black ink, over black chalk.
288 × 428 mm
Louvre, Cabinet des Dessins (27,151)

Literature: Guiffrey-Marcel, vi, no. 4840; *Amis et contemporains de Mariette*, exh. 1967, no. 96, pl. xxiii.

Signed in pen, lower left: *J. Hoüel f.*; lower right, the signatures of *Pierre* and *Cochin*. Inscribed on the mount in ink: *Le plus petit temple d'agrigente qui se voit dans le Couvent St Nicolas à girgenti – planche gravée 234*.

Engraved, with the addition of figures (notably an artist carrying a portfolio under his arm), in vol. iv of the *Voyage pittoresque*, pl. 234, with the title *Petit Temple antique situé dans le couvent de St Nicolas*. The temple, standing in the grounds of the Cistercian abbey of St Nicolas, was traditionally connected with Phalaris, tyrant of Agrigentum in the sixth century BC; but like the so-called 'Tomb of Theron' (see no. 109) it is in fact a Roman shrine or *heroon* of the second century BC. It was later converted by the Normans into a Christian chapel.

Other views of Agrigentum by Houel engraved in the *Voyage pittoresque*, are also in the Louvre. In addition to the three drawings exhibited (nos. 108–10) there are *The Temple of Juno* (27,177), *The Temple of Concord* (27,163 and 27,165) and *The Temple of Castor and Pollux* (27,159).

111 'GARGANTUA'S SEAT' NEAR ROUEN
Gouache over black chalk.
444 × 540 mm
Rouen, Musée des Beaux-Arts (808-1-3)

Provenance: presented by the artist in 1808.

Literature: E. Lebel, *Cat. Musée de Rouen*, 1890, no. 793; E. Minet, *Cat. Musée de Rouen*, 1911, no. 1030; Vlöberg, 1930, pp. 126, 187 f., pl. 162; *Peintres normands de Jouvenet à Lebourg*, exh. Rouen, 1948, no. 273; F. Guéroult, *Dessins français des XVIIè et XVIIIè siècles au Musée de Rouen* (thesis to be published in 1978) no. 63.

Inscribed along lower edge, in pen, by the artist: *Vue de la Roche appelée la chaise de gargantua en 1788 fait par j. p.*

houel en 1788 d'après nature au bord de la rivière entre duclair et . . . .

Houel was attached to his native city of Rouen and returned there on several occasions. In 1788 he drew on the spot this view of one of the natural curiosities of the district, the rock called 'Gargantua's Seat' which hangs over the road between Duclair (a town about ten miles west of Rouen) and the old Porte Cauchoise of Rouen. Among the other drawings presented by Houel to the Rouen Museum in 1808 is a view of the Porte Cauchoise, also dated 1788 (808-1-4).

112 INTERIOR OF THE CAVE AT CAUMONT
*
Brown wash and gouache over a preliminary sketch in pen and brown ink, on blue paper.
298 × 430 mm
Rouen, Musée des Beaux-Arts (909-34-83)

Provenance: Marquis de Chennevières (Lugt 2072: sale, Paris, 4–7 April 1900, lot 239); Le Breton, by whom presented in 1909.

Literature: Le Carpentier, 'Notice sur M. Houel peintre' in the proceedings of the Société d'Emulation, Rouen (1 December 1813, pp. 13 f.); P. de Chennevières, *L'Artiste*, 1895, ix, pp. 96 f.; E. Minet, *Cat. Musée de Rouen*, 1911, no. 1032; Vlöberg, 1930, p. 187; *Peintres normands de Jouvenet à Lebourg*, exh. Rouen, 1948, no. 275; F. Guéroult, *Dessins français des XVIIè et XVIIIè siècles au Musée de Rouen* (thesis to be published in 1978), no. 64.

Signed and dated lower left, in pen: *J. houel f. an 8.* [i.e. from September 1799 to August 1800 in the Revolutionary calendar] *à Caumont.*

This and a companion drawing in the Rouen Museum (likewise part of the Le Breton gift of 1909 and also dating from the period of Houel's visit to Rouen in 1799) represent the stalactitic cavern of Caumont near La Bouille, a few miles from Rouen. They reflect his continuing interest in natural phenomena. F. Gueroult has pointed out that a painting by him of a somewhat similar subject, *A cave at Dieppedalle, used as a salt store,* is also in the Rouen Museum (*French Painting 1774–1830: The Age of Revolution*, exh. Paris (Grand Palais)-Detroit-New York (Metropolitan Museum), 1974–5, no. 101, repr.).

JEAN-JACQUES DE BOISSIEU

(Lyons 1736 – Lyons 1810)

In France in the second-half of the eighteenth century a number of amateur artists were living in the provinces, far from the official art world of Paris with its arguments over aesthetic theory, quietly cultivating a taste for landscape drawing which they often developed in a significant way. Of these amateurs, one of the most gifted was Boissieu, who after studying in Lyons under two local artists, Lombard and Frontier, found himself, in the words of his friend and admirer P.-J. Mariette, 'with no other aim than that of following the prompting of his own genius, with nature as his only guide' (*Abecedario*, i, pp. 143 f.). In 1763/4 he was living in Paris, where he was on friendly terms with Greuze, Joseph Vernet (q.v.), Watelet (q.v.) and Wille (q.v.). In 1765 he accompanied duc Alexandre de la Rochefoucauld to Italy, and it was then that he made his freely drawn sketches of Italian views and popular types. In the following year he went with the Duke, together with the scientist Desmarais, to the Auvergne, in order to investigate the natural history of the region. According to Mariette, 'he spent his time drawing a vast number of details illustrating the geological structure of mountains and the remains of extinct volcanoes'. After a second stay in Paris he succeeded in obtaining an official post in Lyons, where he settled in 1772 for the rest of his life.

Mariette considered Boissieu's paintings 'rather too laborious' but admired his engraved work (amounting to about 140 items) and his drawings. These include studies of heads and *genre* scenes, but above all the views of Lyons and the surrounding country which are remarkable for their quality of fresh and unaffected realism. The chief collections of his drawings are those of the Louvre, the Musée des Beaux-Arts in Lyons, the Staedel Institute of Frankfurt and the Hessisches Landesmuseum in Darmstadt (see Bergsträsser, 1970, pp. 89 ff.).

13 THE BRIDGE AT FRANCHEVILLE

Pen and brown ink and brown and grey wash.
221 × 285 mm
Louvre, Cabinet des Dessins (23,817)

Literature: Guiffrey-Marcel, i, no. 333, repr.; *Le siècle de Louis* xv, exh. Paris, 1934, no. 240; *Amis et contemporains de Mariette*, exh. Paris (Louvre), 1967, no. 98.

Signed in pen, lower left: *J. J. Boissieu*.

The inscription *Auditoire de Francheville* identifies the place as the village of Francheville-le-haut, formerly the seat of a law-court, west of Lyons in the Department of the Rhône. The old houses and the sixteenth-century cross have now disappeared, but the bridge is still there. Mme Perez, who dates the drawing *c.* 1766–70, points out that this place had already attracted the attention of landscape-artists travelling through Lyons including Asselijn, Isaac de Moucheron and Waterloo.

14 A FARMYARD WITH A CART

Brown and grey wash, with some touches of pen and brown ink, over black chalk.

179 × 246 mm
Louvre, Cabinet des Dessins (23,811)

Literature: Guiffrey-Marcel, i, no. 343 repr.; *Le siècle de Louis* xv, exh. Paris, 1934, part of no. 240; *Dessins français du Louvre*, exh. Berne, 1948, no. 62; *Amis et contemporains de Mariette*, exh. Paris (Louvre), 1967, no. 99, pl. xxiv.

'I have always made drawings directly from nature' wrote Boissieu to Wille (A. de Montaiglon, *Lettres de Boissieu à Wille*, n.d., 4 November 1761) 'and for me there is no more delightful pleasure'. His interest in the details of everyday life and his preference for the simplest of subjects place him in the direct line of descent from the Netherlandish masters of the seventeenth century whose works he admired and copied. This wholly objective attitude to reality, reproduced literally with no striving for effect, is a remarkable phenomenon at that date. In the present drawing the influence of Breenbergh is obvious, not only in the choice of subject but also in its rendering in shades of brown and grey wash. Mme Perez dates it before 1765 (*Catalogue de l'oeuvre dessiné de J.-J. de Boissieu*, in preparation).

LOUIS BELANGER

(Paris (?) 1736 – Stockholm 1816)

A number of landscape drawings, mostly in watercolour or gouache, and also a few paintings, bear this signature (sometimes also written 'Bélangé' or 'Bellange'). These bear dates ranging between 1779 (*View of Lyons*, drawing in Orléans: 628) and 1803 (two landscapes in the Nationalmuseum, Stockholm: 1928 cat., nos. 1135–6). Two watercolour landscapes, signed *'Belangé le Jeune'* are in the Louvre (RF 14,631 and 14,632).

Very little is known of this artist. Some of his views are of Italian subjects, but these are not treated with any great topographical accuracy and there is no other indication of his having been there. Others are of Paris and the Ile-de-France, Switzerland and Savoie. He is presumably to be identified with the L. Belanger who exhibited three landscapes at the Royal Academy in London, one in 1790 and two in 1797, describing himself on the former occasion as 'Painter to the Duke of Orléans'. In 1798 he was appointed court painter to the King of Sweden and seems to have spent the rest of his life in Stockholm.

115 LANDSCAPE WITH A RIVER AND A WATERMILL
Pen and brown ink and watercolour.
260 × 496 mm
Orléans, Musée des Beaux-Arts (226)
Provenance: Comte de Bizemont (Lugt 128); Amirale de

Candé, by whom bequeathed in 1888.
Literature: Davoust, 1891, no. 625; *Frankreich vor der Revolution*, exh. Münster, 1973, no. 7, repr. p. 178; *Dessins français du* XVIè *au* XVIIIè *siècle*, exh. Orléans, 1975, no. 7, pl. ci.

JEAN-JACQUES LE BARBIER

(Rouen 1739 – Paris 1826)

After winning the first prize for drawing at the Rouen Academy in 1752 followed by a period in the studio of Pierre in Paris, le Barbier went to Italy, apparently at his own expense. His presence in Rome in 1767–8 and possibly as late as 1772 is established by drawings. In 1776 he was in Switzerland, where in company with Pérignon, Chatelet, Pâris, and others he made drawings of the views, monuments and costumes of the country to illustrate Zurlauben's compilation, *Tableaux de la Suisse ou voyage pittoresque fait dans les treize cantons du Corps Helvétique*, published by Laborde in Paris between 1780 and 1786.

Elected an associate member (*agréé*) of the Académie Royale de Peinture in 1780 and a full member in 1786, he exhibited in the Salon mostly paintings of moralistic subjects. His preference for religious themes and incidents in the earlier history of France (*St Louis*, *Henri* IV etc.) from about 1806–10 foreshadows the painting of the Restoration period; and it was not until 1816, after the return of the Bourbons, that he was elected to the Institut. He made many drawings for book-illustrations, including the works of Racine and Marmontel, though his particular preference seems to have been for idyllic literature ranging from Ovid to Rousseau, Jacques Delille and the Swiss poet Salomon Gessner.

116 LANDSCAPE INSPIRED BY THE GARDENS OF THE VILLA D'ESTE AT TIVOLI

Pen and black ink and grey wash.
399 × 288 mm
Paris, Ecole des Beaux-Arts (1163)

Provenance: J.-E. Gatteaux, (Lugt 852), by whom bequeathed to the Ecole des Beaux-Arts in 1883.

This view is clearly inspired by the fountain under the arcade at the foot of the sloping path to the north-east of the gardens of the Villa d'Este, (cf. no. 80, by Fragonard). Le Barbier's modifications include the placing of a vase on the left-hand pilaster, the addition of three niches with statues in the wall, and the alteration of the entablature over the fountain.

Le Barbier's presence in Rome in 1767 is established by the signature *Le Barbier in Roma 1767* on a painting of *Herdsmen with flocks* at Orléans (no. 841). A drawing

of a *Bacchanal*, also dated 1767, is clearly influenced by the kind of thing that J.-J. Lagrenée was doing in Rome between 1763 and 1769 (Masson Sale, Paris, 7–8 May 1923, lot 114 repr.), and one of a *Procession of Flora*, dated in the same year, has for setting a park like that of an Italian villa (Paris, Galerie Petit, 30 May 1924, lot 86, repr. and Hôtel Drouot, 22 December 1943, lot 65, repr.). Another, of the *Temple of Romulus*, is signed and dated *Rome 1768* (Hôtel Drouot, 22 March 1928, lot 95, repr.). A view inspired by the gardens of the Villa Aldobrandini at Frascati is dated 1772 (Masson Sale, 1923, lot 113, repr.; Breyer Sale, New York, Parke-Bernet, January 1963, lot 250, repr.), but it contains a number of topographical inaccuracies which suggest that it was not necessarily drawn on the spot, and so cannot be regarded as evidence of Le Barbier's presence in Rome as late as that year.

LOUIS-GABRIEL MOREAU
(Paris 1740 – Paris 1806)

Louis Moreau (known as 'Moreau l'aîné' to distinguish him from his younger brother), though one of the best-known Parisian landscape artists of the later eighteenth century never achieved the same official success as his brother Jean-Michel Moreau le jeune (1741–1814). His master, Demachy (see no. 61), was a painter of architectural subjects who transmitted to his pupil the influence of Panini and Servandoni. Moreau began his career in the same way; his first exhibited works, in 1760, were drawings of ruins, and in 1764 he was elected to the Academy of St Luke on the strength of a painting of an architectural subject. He never became a member of the Académie Royale de Peinture, in spite of the fact that until 1804 he regularly exhibited paintings and drawings of landscape. In this, which soon became his speciality, he developed an original talent which owed nothing to Italian influence (he seems, in fact, never to have gone to Italy), taking his subjects from the ordinary French countryside in spring and summer. (It was only very occasionally that he chose an autumnal or wintry scene.) His activity coincided with, and may have contributed to, the freer and less formal view of nature that fostered the 'English' style of landscape garden which he was so fond of representing.

Moreau made a number of landscape etchings (see G. Wildenstein, 1928, pp. 369 ff.) and a great many drawings in every medium. Watercolour and bodycolour were his preferred techniques, and in them he was at his freest and most spontaneous. In his direct vision of nature and his feeling for effects of light and atmosphere he is a forerunner of the English school of landscape at the beginning of the nineteenth century.

117 A FLIGHT OF STEPS IN A PARK

Brush and brown wash, heightened with white.
212 × 172 mm
Louvre, Cabinet des Dessins (RF 29,954)

Provenance: C. du Loup (from whom purchased in 1953).

Literature: Donations et acquisitions, exh. Paris (Louvre) 1955, no. 13; *Pastels et Miniatures du* XVIII*è siècle*, exh. Paris (Louvre) 1964, no. 94.

Signed and dated in pen, lower left: L M 1780.

This drawing and no. 118 are studies for a pair of gouaches, now in the collection of M. Arthur Veil-Picard (Wildenstein, 1923, nos. 144–5; pls. 67–8) which were formerly in the Goncourt Collection. The Goncourts had bought them at the sale of the miniature-painter Carrier: 'The two gouaches in my collection are of the highest quality. I was seized with a desperate longing to possess them as soon as I saw them in the exhibition in the Boulevard des Italiens in 1860' (E. de Goncourt, *La maison d'un artiste*. Paris 1881, i, pp. 121 f.).

Though Moreau frequently enlivened his landscape drawings with small-scale figures, these are never more than subordinate elements. The emphasis is always on nature, as in these drawings where the artist uses the simple combination of brown wash and white bodycolour to suggest the luxuriant intricacy of vegetation and the play of light through the leaves.

118 TALL TREES IN A PARK

Brush and brown wash, heightened with white, on greyish-brown paper.
211 × 168 mm
Louvre, Cabinet des Dessins (RF 29,953)

Provenance: C. du Loup (from whom purchased in 1953).

Literature: Donations et acquisitions, exh. Paris (Louvre) 1955, no. 14; *Pastels et miniatures du* XVIII*è siècle*, exh. Paris (Louvre) 1964, no. 93.

Signed and dated in pen, lower left: L M *1780*. See no. 117.

119 THE PARK AT SAINT-CLOUD

Gouache.
Diameter 102 mm
Louvre, Cabinet des Dessins (RF 30,778)

Provenance: presented by D. David-Weil in 1948.

Literature: Donation D. David-Weil, exh. Paris (Louvre), 1956–7, no. 134, pl. ii; *Vingt ans* d'acquisitions, exh. Paris (Orangerie) 1967–8, no. 495.

This tiny landscape, in which the foliage of the trees is rendered with particular care, with a multitude of little flickering touches which have an almost impressionist effect, illustrates the sharpness of the artist's vision. It may be compared with the two views of a park in the Staedel Institute in Frankfurt (Wildenstein, 1923, nos. 160–1, pl. 76).

120 THE CHATEAU OF VALENÇAY
*
Gouache.
356 × 541 mm
Louvre, Cabinet des Dessins (RF 31,429)

Provenance: bought for the Louvre at a sale in Paris, 4 December 1963, lot 106.

Literature: *Amis et contemporains de Mariette*, exh. Paris (Louvre), 1967, no. 101, repr.; *Vingt ans d'acquisitions*, exh. Paris (Orangerie) 1967–8, no. 494; Sérullaz, Duclaux, Monnier, 1968, no. 61, repr.

Signed and dated lower right, in pen: *L M 1792*.

The château, built in the middle of the sixteenth century by the Etampes family, is famous for having been the country residence of the statesman Talleyrand, who acquired it in 1805 and to whose family it still belongs. In 1792, the date of Moreau's drawing, it belonged to the family of Legendre.

The château is seen from below the surrounding terrace. A companion view, also in the Louvre (RF 31,430), shows it from a different aspect.

CHARLES-PAUL-JEAN-BAPTISTE DE
BOURGEVIN VIALART DE SAINT-MORYS

(Paris 1743 – Ile d'Houat 1795)

The personality of this amateur draughtsman who was also one of the most important French collectors of drawings in the period before the Revolution, is beginning to be better defined. A member of a noble but impoverished family, he received a commission in the army at the age of seventeen, but in 1769 he obtained a legal sinecure through the influence of a rich uncle who in 1778 died leaving him a considerable fortune. This enabled him to take advantage of the numerous sales of works of art held in Paris between 1770 and 1790 to form a large and important collection of pictures, drawings and prints. In 1781 he bought the château of Houdainville, near Beauvais, which was pulled down after the Revolution. Having escaped from France to London in 1790 with his only son Etienne, he joined the royalist forces at Coblentz, where his son married the daughter of Louis xvi's former Minister of Finance, Charles-Alexandre de Calonne. While acting as Quartermaster General of the abortive *émigré* expedition from England which attempted a landing in France in 1795, he died on the island of Houat near Belle-Isle.

Saint-Morys's collections at Houdainville and in his house in the rue Vivienne in Paris were seized by the Revolutionary régime (see Furcy-Raynaud, 1913, pp. 322–6). His drawings by Old Masters, amounting to about twelve thousand, were incorporated into the Musée National and are now in the Louvre. Two collections of facsimile engravings, made by himself, of some of the best of them were later published by his son (see R. Weigel, *Die Werke der Maler in ihren Handzeichnungen*, Leipzig, 1865, pp. 78 f.). Complete copies of these publications are very rare. One in the Bibliothèque Nationale (Inventaire Aa 18) contains a note by Etienne de Saint-Morys (who had returned to France in 1803), saying that the original copper plates from which the prints were made were seized during the Revolution and melted down for cannon.

121 LANDSCAPE WITH A TOWER AND A MILL

* Black chalk with brown wash and touches of watercolour.
115 × 166 mm
Louvre, Cabinet des Dessins (32,801)
Signed and dated lower centre, in pen: *B de St Morys 1771*.

The works of art seized from Saint-Morys in the Revolution included a number of his own drawings, now in the Louvre: some of these are after, or in the manner of, earlier masters, while others are signed and dated original landscape drawings. A landscape with a town in the distance and a view of a convent are both signed and dated '*Cormeil 1771*' (Louvre 32,763, and 32,772); others are dated 1772 (Louvre 32,769) and 1774 (Louvre 37,797 and 32,800). The drawing here exhibited is a product of the artist's imagination rather than a study directly from nature and does not reveal him as a great draughtsman. But his interest in landscape is shown by the number of landscape-drawings by other masters that were in his collection.

JEAN-LOUIS DESPREZ

(Auxerre 1743 – Stockholm 1804)

Desprez was trained as an architect. One of his earliest works was a design for a monumental cemetery in the grandiose visionary manner of Boullée and Ledoux, which he made in 1766 and dedicated to Voltaire. From 1768 to 1776 he studied under the architect Blondel, and in the latter year won the Prix de Rome for architecture. Soon after his arrival in Rome he was invited by the Abbé de Saint Non to collaborate in his *Voyage pittoresque . . . des royaumes de Naples et de Sicile*, and in 1777 and 1778 he travelled widely in southern Italy and Sicily making notes and sketches for illustrations to this book which was eventually published in Paris between 1781 and 1786. Released from the obligation of pursuing practical architectural studies by the then Director of the French Academy in Rome, Vien, and his successor Lagrenée, he was able to devote himself to his activity as an illustrator and architectural draughtsman. In about 1780 he engraved a set of fantastic designs for tombs in aquatint, a technique which he was one of the first to use (*Visionary Architects: Boullée, Ledoux, Lequeu*, exh. Houston etc. 1968, nos. 126–9, repr.) and which he may have learnt from Francesco Piranesi.

The turning-point in his career came with the visit to Rome in 1784 of King Gustav III of Sweden, who invited him to Stockholm to take charge of the design and execution of the scenery for the Royal Opera House. The initial agreement was for two years, but it was eventually renewed for twelve, and in 1788 Desprez was appointed Principal Architect to the King. Gustav's enthusiasm generated many ambitious artistic projects, and Desprez was able to give full rein to his talent in the elaborate scenery that he designed for the Opera and the royal theatres at Gripsholm and Drottningholm and also in large-scale architectural schemes, particularly for the proposed palace at Haga on the outskirts of Stockholm. The assassination of Gustav in 1792 deprived him of his chief patron. Unable to return to France, owing to the Revolution, he looked towards Russia for employment and submitted to Catherine the Great a number of architectural designs in which the Doric and Palladian language of Neo-Classicism was interpreted in a spirit of imaginative and visionary fantasy.

122 VIEW OF STOCKHOLM HARBOUR
*

Pen and black ink and watercolour.
416 × 900 mm
Louvre, Cabinet des Dessins (RF 2133)

Provenance: Count J. P. van Suchtelen (Lugt 2332); marquis de Chennevières (Lugt 2072: sale, Paris, 1898, 5–6 May, lot 42, bought for the Louvre).

Literature: Guiffrey-Marcel, v, no. 3641, repr.; Wollin, 1939, pp. 220 ff.; *L.-J. Desprez*, exh. Paris (Centre culturel suédois) 1974, no. 72.

This large-scale view of Stockholm harbour, showing on the left the Royal Palace, in the centre the North Bridge, and on the right the Arsenal with ships unloading munitions of war, is believed to represent the return of the Swedish army from the Russian campaign of 1790. But whatever the ostensible subject, it is no more than a pretext for a panoramic view of the principal buildings of the city and the activity of the harbour under the diffused light of the northern sky. Characteristic of Desprez is the combination of the precise accuracy of the trained architect and the dramatic sense of the scenic artist.

N. G. Wollin suggests that this drawing and another watercolour, of *The North Bridge from the Gustav-Adolf Square* in the City Museum, Stockholm (Wollin, 1939, fig. 216) are the 'two large views of Stockholm recently presented to His Majesty King Gustav-Adolf', described by Desprez in a list of his works dated 16 August 1798. A replica of the present drawing, with figures by Estenberg, is in the Library at Nogent-sur-Marne (Wollin, op. cit., fig. 215) together with a replica of the companion view.

This drawing bears the collector's mark of Count J. P. Van Suchtelen (1751–1836), a Dutchman who made his career in the Russian army from 1783 and who was Russian ambassador to Sweden in 1814. 'At the sale of a collection formed in Sweden by a Russian who was ambassador in Sweden and in England, which was brought back from Russia by a French engineer, M. Alexandre Garnier' writes Chennevières in one of the articles on his collection which he contributed to *L'Artiste* between 1894 and 1897. 'I was able to buy several things of particular importance for the history of art in those countries, of which the most important is my great panorama of Stockholm by Desprez – a masterpiece of delicate drawing and of perspective'.

JOSEPH-BENOIT SUVÉE

(Bruges 1743 – Rome 1807)

Suvée's development followed the same lines as the arts in general during the last thirty years of the eighteenth century. Born in Bruges, he studied in Paris under Vien (q.v.). In 1771 he was awarded the Prix de Rome for painting in preference to David, and in the same year went to Rome where he remained until 1777. There he came into contact with the first generation of artists influenced by the international Neo-Classic movement. After his return to Paris he was elected associate member (*agréé*) of the Académie Royale de Peinture in 1779 and a full member in the following year. He exhibited at every Salon from 1779 to 1796, pictures painted for the King, tapestry-cartoons for the Gobelins factory, paintings of religious subjects and portraits. His works include *The Vestal Emilia* (Louvre), *The Festival of the God Pales* (Rouen), *Aeneas and Creusa* (Louvre), *The Death of Coligny* (Dijon) and *Cornelia, Mother of the Gracchi* (Louvre). Having passed through all the stages of the regular academic career, he was appointed Director of the French Academy in Rome in 1792, though he did not take up the position until 1801. It was he who was responsible for transferring the Academy to its present seat in the Villa Medici.

With hardly an exception, Suvée's landscape drawings, like those of most of the history-painters of his generation, were made in the course of his period of study in Rome. His preferred medium was red chalk until about 1775, after which he used black chalk. His drawings, characteristic though their style is, are often confused with those of L. Chäys (or Chaix): the two artists often drew the same view at the same time, and sometimes seem even to have copied one another's drawings.

23 A TENT ON THE SEA-SHORE

Black chalk.
324 × 445 mm
Louvre, Cabinet des Dessins (32,983)

Provenance: Comte d'Orsay; confiscated during the Revolution and placed in the museum at Versailles (Lugt 2239: see below); transferred to the Louvre in 1823.

Literature: L'Italia vista dai pittori francesi, exh. Rome-Turin, 1961, pp. 17 f. and no. 322.

From May to October 1777 Suvée was in Sicily as the travelling companion to Pierre-Gaspard Grimod, comte d'Orsay. This drawing is one of eight in the Louvre (32,981 to 32,988) which record their journey into what was still virtually unknown territory (cf. also the drawings by Houel, Desprez and Chatelet). The traditional identification of the place as Terracina is certainly incorrect: the Rock of Terracina is much larger and on the edge of the open sea, not an inlet as is clearly represented in the drawing. The place is likely to be in Sicily, perhaps somewhere on the east coast between Messina and Catania, rather than on the mainland. Tents of this kind were used for bathing from in Sicily well before this period. The Benedictines of Catania, for example, used them on the beach (see G. Policastro, *Catania nel settecento*, 1950, p. 206).

M. Deloche's identification (Guiffrey-Marcel i, p. 139) of the collector's mark (Lugt 2239) on this drawing and the other seven in the Louvre as that of the English engraver Robert Strange, was followed by Lugt only with some hesitation. In fact, the mark is that put on the drawings and prints confiscated under the Revolution in the department of Seine-et-Oise and deposited in the Museum at Versailles. Most, if not all, of these came from the château d'Orsay and consisted of the collection confiscated after the escape of the comte d'Orsay to Germany.

PIERRE-ADRIEN PARIS

(Besançon 1745 – Besançon 1819)

After training as an architect, Pâris went to Rome in 1769. He had failed to win the Prix de Rome, but was given a special grant by the King and accommodated in the French Academy. He remained there for five years, and acted as *cicerone* to Bergeret de Grandcourt and Fragonard when they came to Rome in 1773 (see no. 83).

In 1778 he succeeded M.-A. Challe as Draughtsman to the King and in 1780 was elected to the Académie Royale de Peinture. In 1783 he returned for a short time to Italy, where he came to know the archaeologist Séroux d'Agincourt and the Abbé de Saint-Non, who employed him to make some of the illustrations for the *Voyage pittoresque . . . de Naples et de Sicile*. On his return to Paris in the following year he was diverted from these archaeological interests by being appointed Architect of the *Menus-Plaisirs* and the Opera by Louis XVI. His duties involved 'planning and designing all the court festivities and also the scenery for all the plays performed for the King at Versailles, Fontainebleau, Marly and Choisy, as well as in Paris'. The design of these spectacles – the last ones of the *ancien régime* – encouraged Pâris to give full rein to his capacity for imaginary fantasy (see the drawing exhibited). His actual architectural works were few in number. He helped complete the cathedral at Orléans in the gothic style, and for Louis XVI made plans for the remodelling of the château at Versailles (not executed).

During the Revolution he left Paris and spent the next fifteen years in retirement, occupying himself mostly with gardening and translating works on agriculture. In 1806 he went again to Rome, and for a short time acted as temporary Director of the French Academy. In 1817 he finally returned to France.

From his various journeys to Italy Pâris brought back an important collection of drawings, mostly Italian views, by himself and by his contemporaries, friends and pupils, which he bequeathed to his native city of Besançon. The collection was particularly rich in drawings by Hubert Robert and Fragonard: it included the views of the Villa d'Este that had belonged to Saint-Non and other drawings by Fragonard purchased at the Bergeret de Grandcourt sale in 1786.

---

124 'THE GARDEN OF CYTHERE'

Pen and brown ink and watercolour.
320 × 408 mm
Besançon, Musée des Beaux-Arts (D. 2966)

Provenance: P.-A. Pâris, by whom bequeathed to the Municipal Library of Besançon in 1819. Transferred to the Musée des Beaux-Arts in 1919.

Literature: Cornillot, 1957, no. 119, with previous literature.

Mlle Cornillot connects this drawing – evidently a design for stage scenery – with a ballet by Glück entitled *Cythère Assiégée*. This was first produced in 1775, but it is not impossible that it was revived later with new scenery. M. Grüber, who has made a special study of Pâris's activity at the *Menus-Plaisirs*, points out that the more personal aspect of his stage design lay in his settings for plays with contemporary subject-matter. In these he displayed his Neo-Classic taste in settings of gardens in the 'Romano-English' style – 'tempiettos doriques, ruines composées' – of which he was particularly proud.

The most complete collection of Pâris's designs for scenery is still in the Municipal Library in Besançon (Recueil no. 483). A drawing in red chalk is in the Musée Borely in Marseilles (*Donation Feuillat de Borsat*, exh. Marseilles, 1969, no. 107, repr.) and a 'study for the foliage decorating the duchesse de Bourbon's theatre' is in the Kunstbibliothek in Berlin (HdZ 2914; Berkenhagen, 1970, p. 385).

JEAN-PIERRE NORBLIN DE LA GOURDAINE

(Misy-Faut-Yonne 1745 – Paris 1830)

A pupil of Francesco Casanova, Norblin was invited in 1774 to Poland by Prince Adam Czartoryski. It was here that the main part of his career was spent. He worked for the great Polish families – the Czartoryskis in their palace at Powaski and the Radziwills in the Sanctuary of Minerva at Lowicz – and for King Stanislaus Augustus who ennobled him and in 1785 gave him the title of court-painter, and commissioned from him a picture of the *Battle of Zborow*. He also founded a Royal Academy of Painting in Warsaw modelled on the one in Paris. The events of 1794 in Poland inspired him to paint scenes of battles and revolutionary tumults in the manner of his early master Casanova. At the beginning of the nineteenth century he returned for good to France and devoted himself to making etchings in the manner of Rembrandt (ninety-three are listed in Hillemacher's catalogue of 1877) and drawings of Parisian daily life and manners, of which an important group is in the Musée Carnavalet.

125 THE QUAI DES THEATINS AND THE PONT-ROYAL IN PARIS

Brown wash and watercolour over pencil and pen and ink, heightened with white. The sheet is made up of several pieces of paper.
360 × 530 mm
Paris, Musée Carnavalet (D. 7030)

Provenance: no. 32 in the artist's posthumous sale, Paris, 1830, 14 May: 'Vue du quai Voltaire, dessin à l'aquarelle, effet de lune'.

Literature: Fournier-Sarlovèze, 1911, ii, p. 288; Batowski, 1911, p. 170; *Trois siècles de dessin parisien*, exh. Paris (Musée Carnavalet), 1946, no. 284; *Paris und das Pariser Leben*, exh. Vienna-Berne, 1950, no. 156; *Dessins parisiens des XIXè et XXè siècles*, Paris (Musée Carnavalet), 1976, no. 104.

Signed and dated in pen, on the waggon lower centre: N.B. 77.

The Quai des Théatins (Quai Voltaire from 1791) took its name from the religious order whose house stood on the site of the present nos 15–25. Voltaire died in 1778 in the Hôtel Villette (no. 27), where he had lived as a young man in 1724. The Pont-Royal, built between 1685 and 1689, crosses the Seine by the south-western extremity of the Louvre (the Pavillon de Flore).

Apart from its value as a topographical record, the most striking feature of the drawing, referred to in the description in the sale catalogue, is the rendering of moonlight. Norblin was particularly interested in effects of light and his nocturnal subjects have a certain Pre-Romantic flavour; others are the drawings of *The Guitar Player*, dated 1823, and *The Street singer* (Musée Carnavalet D. 7024–5; *Dessins Parisiens*, exh. 1976, nos. 108 and 109, both repr.).

126 THE TERRACE OF THE TUILERIES GARDENS
*

Pen and brown ink and brown and grey wash.
340 × 420 mm
Paris, Musée Carnavalet (D. 7027)

Literature: Fournier-Sarlovèze, 1911, ii, p. 287; Batowski, 1911, p. 170; *Paysage français de Poussin à Corot*, exh. Paris (Petit Palais), 1925, no. 622; *Trois siècles de dessin parisien*, exh. Paris (Musée Carnavalet), 1946, no. 278; *Paris und das Pariser Leben*, exh. Vienna-Berne, 1950, no. 151; *Dessins parisiens des XIXè et XXè siècles*, exh. Paris (Musée Carnavalet), 1976, no. 102.

Signed and dated: *Norblin 1807*

A companion drawing in the same technique, dated 1808, also in the Musée Carnavalet, represents the Tuileries Gardens (D. 7028: *Dessins parisiens*, exh. 1976, no. 103 repr.). Though these compositions to some extent continue the early eighteenth-century tradition of the *fête galante* and the theme of figures under trees which Norblin treated in his paintings for the Czartoryski family in the Powaski Palace, they reveal the sharper and more down-to-earth vision that characterized his style after his return to France. The then fashionable Neo-Classic taste is apparent not only in the women's dresses but also in the way in which some of the groups of figures are inspired by Antique sculpture.

The statue which appears in the present drawing is that of *Spring* by F. Barrois, one of the *Four Seasons* placed in the gardens in about 1680 when they were replanned by Le Nôtre.

FRANÇOIS-ANDRÉ VINCENT

(Paris 1746 – Paris 1816)

Vincent's career, like that of Suvée, spans a period of stylistic transition. He was a pupil of Vien (q.v.), and the painting that won him the Prix de Rome in 1768, *Germanicus quelling a mutiny in his camp*, is still in the tradition of Boucher and Greuze. From 1771 to 1775 he was in Rome, where he studied 'the Antique and the Great Masters'. He also painted some portraits, including one of Houel (see p. 80) now in the Rouen Museum, and drew some striking caricatures of his friends, now mostly in the Louvre, the Musée Carnavalet and the Musée Atger at Montpellier. His interest in landscape seems not to have persisted after he left Rome, for all his known landscape drawings date from that period.

It is for his portraits that Vincent is chiefly remembered today, rather than for the large 'machines' of episodes of French history and from ancient history and mythology on which his contemporary reputation was founded and even caused him to be compared with Jacques-Louis David.

127 THE FARNESE GARDENS ON THE PALATINE, WITH AN ARTIST SKETCHING

Red chalk.
273 × 392 mm
Orléans, Musée des Beaux-Arts (D. 1141)

Provenance: L. Belot; purchased by the Museum at his sale in 1878.

Literature: Paysage français de Poussin à Corot, exh. Paris, 1925, no. 707; *Frankreich vor der Revolution*, exh. Münster, 1973, no. 113; *Dessins français du* XVIè *au* XVIIIè *siècle*, exh. Orleans, 1975, no. 118, pl. lxxxix, Méjanès, 1976, p. 144.

Signed and dated in pen, lower right: *Vincent*.

The draughtsman and his companion are on the slope of the Farnese Gardens on the Palatine Hill. Similar figures enliven the landscape in other drawings by Vincent: one in black chalk dated 1774, which has just entered the museum at Rouen as part of the Baderou gift; and another in the same technique and dated 1775, of a stream near Tivoli, in the Fondation Custodia (Institut Néerlandais). Paris (Méjanès, 1976, fig. 15). It seems to have been in about 1774/5 that Vincent, like Suvée, gave up using red chalk for landscape-drawings in favour of black chalk.

A group of drawings by Vincent in red chalk form part of the bequest of his fellow-pupil in Rome, P.-A. Pâris, to the Museum at Besançon (Recueil 453).

A view of a harbour in the Hamburg Kunsthalle (24,501) is in pen and brown ink heightened with white on blue paper. This technique, unusual for Vincent, is that of two drawings described in the catalogue of his posthumous sale (Paris, 1816, lots 66, 164).

JACQUES-LOUIS DAVID

(Paris 1748 – Brussels 1825)

David is above all remembered for his leading part in the final triumph of the Neo-Classic tendency in French historical painting. His *Oath of the Horatii* of 1785 was one of the first of a long series of pictures treating subjects from Ancient history or the events of the Revolution and Empire in an heroic style founded on the moral ideals and aesthetic principles of Antiquity, as then understood. He was not the originator of this aesthetic doctrine nor was he all at once converted to it. It had been formulated in the 1760's in Rome by an international circle of archaeologists and painters, including Winckelmann, Raffael Mengs, Pompeo Batoni, Gavin Hamilton and Benjamin West. With the exception of Laurent Pecheux and Etienne La Vallée-Poussin – both relatively minor personalities – French painters in Rome seem to have been little attracted by Neo-Classicism before the arrival in 1775 of J.-M. Vien, the new Director of the French Academy and David's master. David himself came there in the same year and remained until 1780. His Roman sketchbooks (Louvre; Stockholm; Fogg Museum, Harvard) illustrate the development of his taste, and how his interest in earlier masters, ranging from Paolo Veronese to Caravaggio, gradually gave way to the realization of the significance of Antique sculpture. They also show that in common with all French students in Rome in the eighteenth century, he was interested in landscape, and that he interpreted the scenery of Rome in a highly individual way. But as with almost all the History painters of his generation, this interest did not persist after his return to France. The famous view of the Luxembourg Gardens (Louvre) which he painted during his imprisonment in 1796 might be described as the exception that proves the rule. He also drew some views of Switzerland in 1815, at the beginning of his exile before he settled in Brussels (see Sérullaz-Calvet, 1965, pp. 65 ff.).

28 A GRANARY OR WAREHOUSE, PROBABLY IN ROME

Pen and black ink and grey wash, over black chalk.
150 × 216 mm
Louvre, Cabinet des Dessins (26,082 bis)

Provenance: J.-L. David (sale, Paris, 1828); E. and J. David (Lugt 839 and 1437; sale, Paris, 11 March 1855, bought for the Louvre).

Literature: Reiset, 1869, no. 652; J.-L. and J. David, 1880, p. 652; Guiffrey-Marcel, iv, no. 3211, repr.; *Gros, ses amis, ses élèves*, exh. Paris (Petit Palais), 1936, no. 527; *David*, exh. London (Tate Gallery)-Manchester, 1948, no. 29 b; *David*, exh. Paris (Orangerie), 1948, no. 83; *L'Italia vista dai pittori francesi del XVIII e XIX secolo*, exh. Rome-Turin, 1961, no. 105 (Turin, no. 97); *Dessins français de 1750 à 1825: le Néo-Classicisme*, exh. Paris (Louvre), 1972, no. 47, pl. xxiii.

David's landscape drawings are almost all of buildings or townscapes, often with flights of steps or colonnades which offer scope for effects of perspective. Some of them (e.g. the drawing exhibited and Louvre 26,110 and 26,111: Guiffrey-Marcel, iv, nos. 3267-8, both repr.) have every appearance of being views drawn on the spot in Rome, but the exact locations cannot be identified with any certainty. At least one (Louvre 26,082: Guiffrey-Marcel, iv, no. 3210, repr.) is a kind of *capriccio*, made up of the Castel Sant'Angelo and a bridge composed of elements from the Ponte Molle and the Ponte Salaro. Others (e.g. Louvre 26,081, 26,081 ter: Guiffrey-Marcel, iv, nos. 3212-3, both repr.) are 'visionary' architectural compositions.

Like Valenciennes (q.v.), who was in Rome at the same time, David did not draw in the red or black chalk which had been the preferred medium of earlier generations of draughtsmen (and which Vincent and Suvée were still using) but in pen and wash – a technique which enabled him to conceive his architectural compositions in terms of broad masses of light and shade.

The unadorned simplicity and utilitarian purpose of industrial and functional architecture were qualities that made it particularly congenial to the aesthetic and social ideals of Neo-Classicism. In the present drawing, David's approach to the subject is the very reverse of Picturesque. His attention is concentrated on the relation of the principal masses, the rhythm of the roofs and simple windows and arcading, and the natural setting; the result has the monumental simplicity of the buildings in the backgrounds of paintings by Domenichino or Poussin.

CLAUDE-LOUIS CHATELET

(Paris (?) c. 1750 – Paris 1795)

Nothing is known of the circumstances of Chatelet's birth and artistic training (he is not recorded as a pupil at the Académie Royale) and very little about his career except that he was principally active as a topographical draughtsman and book-illustrator. He made some of the drawings for Laborde and Zurlauben's *Tableaux de la Suisse* (1780–2) and many for Saint-Non's *Voyage pittoresque . . . de Naples et Sicile* (1781–6). Some of the latter are in the British Museum and in the museums at Caen, Montpellier, etc.

A few paintings by him are known: a series of views of Versailles, made for Mique's publication of 1781, were in the Esmerian Collection (sale, Paris, 1973, 6 June, lot 65) and of nocturnal fêtes at the Petit Trianon (Carnavalet, Versailles, E. de Rothschild Coll.). Two sea-pieces are in the museum at Fontainebleau, and a painting based on one of his Sicilian watercolours was recently sold in Paris (Hôtel Drouot, 1968, 9 December, lot 49, repr.).

The best-documented episode in Chatelet's life is his death. A fervent Jacobin, he was a member of the Revolutionary Tribunal which was responsible for the Terror. In the reaction which followed the fall of Robespierre, he was guillotined on 7 May 1795 (not 1794 as is usually stated). The official record of his death gives his age as forty-five (P. Jarry, 1929, pp. 351 f.).

129 A SCENE FROM ROUSSEAU'S NOVEL 'LA NOUVELLE HELOISE'

Pen and brown ink and grey wash over black chalk.
351 × 285 mm
Louvre, Cabinet des Dessins (RF 35,518)

Provenance: acquired in 1972.

The gestures of the figures, and their position on a rocky ledge overlooking a lake, suggest that the subject may be the episode described in Letter XVII of Jean-Jacques Rousseau's novel, *Lettres de deux amans habitans d'une petite ville au pied des Alpes* (Amsterdam, 1761), better known as *Julie, ou la Nouvelle Heloïse*: the heroine, Julie d'Etange, who has been married for ten years to the baron de Wolmar, encountering her former lover Saint-Preux in the place where they had first confessed their mutual affection.

Rousseau evoked the background of the episode in his novel, and gave careful instructions about it to Gravelot, the earliest illustrator of the book. He describes it as 'a lonely spot, a wild and barren retreat, surrounded by those overpowering natural beauties by which sensitive hearts are moved, but which others find horrifying' and draws a deliberate contrast between 'these huge magnificent objects' (the lake and the mountains) and 'the charming pastoral gaiety' of the place where the two lovers find one another. This passage demonstrates the extent of his contribution to the sentimental, pre-romantic, feeling for nature of the later eighteenth century, and the then current variant of the 'pathetic fallacy' according to which the landscape setting of an action was expected to echo the emotions of the participants.

PIERRE-HENRI DE VALENCIENNES
(Toulouse 1750 – Paris 1819)

Valenciennes received his early training at the Academy in Toulouse and under Gabriel-François Doyen in Paris. In 1777 he settled in Rome, where he remained, apart from an excursion to Sicily and a brief return to Paris in 1780–1, for seven years. By 1785 he was back in Paris. Two years later he was elected to the Académie Royale and began exhibiting regularly at the Salon. In 1812 he was appointed Professor of Perspective at the Ecole des Beaux-Arts, and in 1816 he was one of those instrumental in founding the Prix de Rome for landscape. In 1817 he seems to have gone again to Rome, but there is no evidence that he ever travelled further afield, to Greece and the Near East, as was once supposed. He was particularly influential as a teacher, and his book *Elements de Perspective Pratique . . . suivis de Réflexions et Conseils à un élève sur la Peinture et particulièrement sur le genre du Paysage* (1799–1800; 2nd, enlarged ed., 1820) became the bible of the Neo-Classic landscape painters.

The years that Valenciennes spent in Rome between 1777 and 1784 were of crucial importance in his development. He brought back from Italy a large number of sketchbooks and oil-sketches, now mostly in the Louvre and the Bibliothèque Nationale. These provided, as it were, the raw material of his art. As he himself wrote: 'though one may stay in Rome for years, finally one has to return home; but one should make good use of one's time there and bring back a rich harvest of sketches and drawings, to be used whenever necessary once one is no longer in that beautiful land which electrifies the soul and encourages one's talent to grow'. Valenciennes – 'the David of Landscape' – was the chief exponent of the theory and practice of 'historic landscape'. By ennobling and idealizing nature to create a setting consonant in mood with the elevated actions or sentiments of his figures, he aspired to raise landscape to the level of history painting, then considered the highest and noblest branch of the art. But though the large-scale Salon pictures which he produced in accordance with these theories contain many beautifully observed and sensitively rendered passages, his attempt must be regarded as an heroic failure. He would hardly be remembered today except as a theorist of limited historic and academic interest, had it not been for the acquisition by the Louvre in 1930 of a collection of about one hundred and twenty-five landscape oil-sketches, ten of which are here exhibited. These show him in a very different light. They were given to the Louvre by the Princesse de Croÿ, whose grandfather, M. de l'Espine, had bought them at the artist's posthumous sale in 1819 and at that of his pupil Anne-Louis Girodet in 1825. That they should have been kept together in this way is significant: like Desportes before him and Corot later, Valenciennes regarded his sketches not as finished works made for exhibition and sale, but as part of the working material of his studio, to be used for reference, as a source of inspiration, and (in his case particularly) for instructing pupils. In them the landscape of the nineteenth century is foreshadowed. Rome is not seen through the archaeological-romantic eyes of a Fragonard or a Hubert Robert: her ruins and monuments are treated simply as elements in a landscape composition, with neither more nor less emphasis than the characterless modern houses surrounding them. In making his sketches, Valenciennes was above all concerned with capturing the transient effects of light and atmosphere; he often painted the same view more than once, at various times of day or in differing weather conditions. The effects are indeed sometimes so transient that it is difficult to see how the sketch could have been made on the spot. It seems probable that some of them at least were executed in the studio on the basis of rapid pencil sketches augmented with written colour-notes (see P. Conisbee in *Burlington Magazine* cxviii (1976), p. 336).

It has often been observed how strikingly these sketches by Valenciennes resemble Corot's Roman sketches of nearly half a century later. It is true that a direct link between the two artists exists in the person of Achille-Etna Michallon (q.v.), who had been a pupil of one and was to become the master of the other, but making studies of this kind seems to have been a well-established tradition in France: Desportes was sketching in this way at the beginning of the eighteenth century (see nos. 6–17), and there is evidence that Joseph Vernet was doing the same in Rome in the 1740's. Valenciennes himself records that he took lessons in perspective from Vernet during his temporary return to Paris in 1780–1; and it may well be, as Mr Conisbee suggests (op. cit.), that Vernet also instructed him in the art of landscape sketching in oil. If so, his sketches would date from his later years in Rome, from 1781/2 to 1784. The Louvre sketches were exhibited all together for the first time in the spring of 1976. On that occasion they were the subject of an admirable study by Mme Geneviève Lacambre (*Le petit journal des grandes expositions*, N.S. no. 30), who rearranged them according to a list made by Valenciennes himself which she had discovered in one of his sketchbooks in the Louvre, and the old numbering inscribed on the sketches themselves. The sketches can now be divided into three main groups: A, those listed by Valenciennes (nos. 131–7); B, those that came from the studio of Anne-Louis Girodet; C, sketches that Valenciennes classified in groups of a dozen, and which are for the most part replicas (nos. 139–40).

130 SKETCHBOOK
*

The sketchbook consists of ninety-four leaves, measuring 273 × 95 mm. All but the first are numbered from 1 to 93. The sketches, on the *recto* of each sheet except the last which is drawn on both sides, are in pencil with pen and brown ink and wash or pen and black ink and grey wash. On the spine of the vellum cover is inscribed in brown ink, by the artist: LIVRE A DESSINER P. DEVALENCIENNES 1778 ROME.
Louvre, Cabinet des Dessins (RF 12,966)

Provenance: Valenciennes Sale, Paris, 1819, part of lot 15; P. Ch. de l'Espine; Vicomte A. E. de l'Espine; Comte M. E. O. de l'Espine; Princesse Louis de Croÿ, by whom presented in 1930.

Literature: Oeuvres provenant des donations faites par Madame la Princesse Louis de Croÿ et Monsieur Louis Devillez, exh. Paris (Orangérie), 1930–1, no. 134; Venturi, 1941, p. 98.

The page shown (f. 14) is inscribed by the draughtsman in ink: '*sur la route d'Orviete*'. The same inscription occurs on the preceding eight leaves and on the following leaf, while nos. 16 and 17 are inscribed: '*sur la route d'Orviete en retournant à Rome*'. These twelve leaves are thus clearly a record of an excursion made by Valenciennes in the year after his arrival, to Orvieto, about 60 miles north of Rome. The word *composé* inscribed on some of the drawings in the book presumably indicates that they were not drawn directly from nature. Three of the drawings are after fresco landscapes by Gaspar Dughet in the church of S. Martino ai Monti – the only copies after other masters that occur in Valenciennes's known sketchbooks.

In addition to the group of oil-sketches, Princesse Louis de Croÿ's gift included a quantity of separate drawings and a further eight sketchbooks. One of these, dated 1775 and containing views in Paris and Touraine, is from the period before the artist's visit to Italy (RF 12,971). The others provide valuable evidence for his movements between 1778 and 1781: Rome and the surrounding country (RF 12,965, 12,967, 12,969), Naples and Sicily in 1779 (RF 12,968), Florence, Lombardy, Geneva and Lyons in 1781 (RF 12,972–3). The remaining two contain only manuscript material, including a list of the oil-sketches which has enabled the artist's own classification to be reconstructed.

131 RUINS IN THE GARDEN OF THE VILLA FARNESE
*
Oil on paper.
263 × 404 mm
Louvre, Département des Peintures (RF 3008)

Provenance: Valenciennes Sale, Paris, 1819, part of lot 7; then as for no. 130.

Literature: Sterling-Adhémar, 1961, no. 1846, pl. 735; Lacambre, 1976, no. A 5.

Inscribed above in pen, on the old mount: *à la villa farnez – 64*; on the back of the mount, in black chalk: *79* and in pencil: *5*.

132 A TREE-GROWN CLIFF

Oil on paper.
245 × 334 mm
Louvre, Département des Peintures (RF 2993)

Provenance: as for no. 130.

Literature: Sterling-Adhémar, 1961, no. 1937, pl. 750; Lacambre, 1976, no. A 9.

Inscribed on the *verso* in black chalk: *89* and in pencil: *no. 9*.

A replica is also in the Louvre (RF 2920; Lacambre, 1976, no. C 43).

133 MONTE CAVO IN CLOUDS

Oil on paper.
151 × 285 mm
Louvre, Département des Peintures (RF 2941)

Provenance: as for no. 131.

Literature: Sterling-Adhémar, 1961, no. 1915, pl. 747; Lacambre, 1976, no. A 11.

Inscribed on the back of the old mount in black chalk, underlined in red chalk: *9*, and in pencil: *no. 11*.

A replica, also in the Louvre (RF 2912; Lacambre, 1976, no. C 34 repr.) is inscribed 'Rocca di Papa', the name of the village in the Alban Hills from which the view was taken. Other views of Monte Cavo are RF 3025 and RF 2938 (Lacambre nos. A 15, A 38).

134 LAKE NEMI

Oil on paper.
240 × 333 mm
Louvre, Département des Peintures (RF 3026)

Provenance: as for no. 131.

Literature: Sterling-Adhémar, 1961, no. 1883, pl. 741; Lacambre, 1976, no. A 18 (repr.).

Inscribed above, in pencil on the old mount: *il lago di nemi*; on the back of the mount, in black chalk: *64* and in pencil: *no. 18*.

135 ROME: THE TIBER AND ST PETER'S UNDER A
* STORMY SKY ('ROME: ORAGE CHAUD')

Oil on paper.
260 × 383 mm
Louvre, Département des Peintures (RF 3001)

Provenance: as for no. 131.

Literature: Sterling-Adhémar, 1961, no. 1824, pl. 730; Lacambre, 1976, no. A 44.

Inscribed on the back of the old mount, in black chalk: *66* and in pencil: *43*.

136 LANDSCAPE WITH CYPRESSES

Oil on paper.
160 × 255 mm
Louvre, Département des Peintures (RF 2939)

Provenance: as for no. 131.

Literature: Sterling-Adhémar, 1961, no. 1936, pl. 750; Lacambre, 1976, no. A 58 (repr.).

Inscribed above, on the old mount, in black chalk: *6* and in pencil: *58*.

137 THE CONVENT OF THE ARACOELI IN ROME
*

Oil on paper.
172 × 260 mm
Louvre, Département des Peintures (RF 3027)

Provenance: as for no. 131.

Literature: Sterling-Adhémar, 1961, no. 1838, pl. 733; Lacambre, 1976, no. A 59 (repr.).

Inscribed above, on the old mount, in pen: *frati della Reccely a Ro*; on the back of the mount, the inscription repeated, with numbers *10* (in black chalk) and *59* (in pencil).

The convent – a once fortified building also sometimes known as the *Torre di Paolo* III – stood on the north side of the Capitol Hill, adjoining the church of S. Maria in Aracoeli. It was destroyed at the end of the last century to make way for the monument to King Victor Emmanuel II. An old photograph of it is reproduced in P. Portoghesi, *Roma: un altra città*, Rome, 1968, p. 129; and a drawing of it by Valenciennes, showing the north side of the church and the conspicuous umbrella-pine, is on f. 6 of his sketchbook in the Bibliothèque Nationale.

Another oil-sketch, from the same point of view but with the sun at a different angle, is also in the Louvre (RF 3013; Lacambre, 1976, no. A 26, repr.).

138 STUDY OF CLOUDS, FROM THE QUIRINAL
*

Oil on paper.
256 × 381 mm
Louvre, Département des Peintures (RF 2987)

Provenance: A.-L. Girodet (sale, Paris, 1825, part of lot 458); vicomte A. E. de l'Espine; then as for no. 131.

Literature: Sterling-Adhémar, 1961, no. 1834, pl. 732; Lacambre, 1976, no. B 15.

Inscribed above, on the old mount, in pen: *a monte cavallo Roma no. 67*; on the back, in black chalk: *73*, in pencil: *458* and in pen: *458–460*.

Mme Lacambre pointed out that this sketch is one of the series that had belonged to Anne-Louis Girodet, who on his return from Italy in 1795 established himself in a studio next-door to that of Valenciennes. She suggests that the sketches were probably given to Girodet by Valenciennes at about that time.

139 VIEW FROM THE VILLA FARNESE

Oil on paper.

261 × 387 mm

Louvre, Département des Peintures (RF 2918)

Provenance: as for no. 131.

Literature: Sterling-Adhémar, 1961, no. 1853, pl. 739; Lacambre, 1976, no. C 14.

Inscribed in pen, on the back of the old mount: *A villa Farnèse no. 2 de la 2è douz.*

This sketch and no. 140 belong to series C, which consists of replicas probably painted after Valenciennes's return from Rome, and which he classified in groups of a dozen each. No. 139 is a replica of a sketch from the Girodet group (RF 3009; Lacambre, 1976, no. B 13).

140 STUDY OF SKY AND ROOF-TOPS IN ROME

Oil on paper.

170 × 410 mm

Louvre, Département des Peintures (RF 2898)

Provenance: as for no. 131.

Literature: Sterling-Adhémar, 1961, no. 1927; Lacambre, 1976, no. C 37.

Inscribed above on the old mount, in pen: *no 37 à Rome no. 1er de la 4è douzaine* (repeated on back).

A replica of a sketch in group A (RF 2940; Lacambre, 1976, no. A 39). The subject had previously been described as *Ruins in a plain, at dusk*, but Valenciennes himself gave the earlier version the title *ciel et toits*.

ALEXANDRE-JEAN NOEL

(Brie-Comte-Robert 1752 – Paris 1834)

A pupil of Joseph Vernet and of J.-A. Silvestre, Noël specialized in marine subjects. Most of the pictures that he exhibited were of sea-ports, naval battles, storms at sea and shipwrecks. In 1768, when he was only sixteen, he accompanied the famous astronomer, the Abbé Chappe d'Auteroche, on a scientific expedition to Lower California in the capacity of draughtsman. The drawings that he brought back with him, ten of which are in the Louvre (Duclaux, 1975, nos. 168–77, repr.), are of great documentary interest (see the article by M. N. Benisovitch in *The Art Quarterly*, xvii (1954), pp. 138 ff.). He later went to Spain and, in 1780, Portugal (Benisovitch, 1952, pp. 118 f.), and made views of the harbours of those countries. He also painted and drew landscapes in France, including views of Paris (Musée Carnavalet) and Rouen.

141 VIEW OF ROUEN

Black chalk.
302 × 503 mm
Paris, Musée du Petit Palais (Inv. Dutuit 1063)

Provenance: E. and A. Dutuit, by whom bequeathed in 1902.

Literature: Lapauze, Gronkowski, Fauchier-Magnan, 1925, no. 1020.

Inscribed on the old mount, in pen: *Vue du port de Rouen du côté du Cours Dauphin Noël fecit 1777.*

Two other drawings by Noël, in the same technique as the one exhibited and likewise dated 1777, are in the Musée du Petit Palais. One is another view of Rouen, the other of the Mont Saint-Adrien seen from St Ouen, on the Seine a little way downstream from Rouen.

VICTOR-JEAN NICOLLE

(Paris 1754 – Paris 1826)

Though many French artists responded to the charm of Italy, Nicolle was exceptional in being so impressed by the beauty and magnificence of Rome that he devoted the greater part of his activity to the representation of every aspect of the city. His work does not consist exclusively of Italian views, however, for there are drawings by him of France and especially of Paris. He had been trained in Paris, first at the Free School of Drawing where in 1771 he won the first prize for perspective, followed by a period in the studio of an architect, Petit-Rudel. He went several times to Rome between 1787 and 1798 and again between 1806 and 1811, and he also visited Florence, Naples, Venice and Bologna (Boucher, 1923, pp. 98 f. and 104).

In the course of his travels, Nicolle must have come across Vernet, Fragonard and Hubert Robert, but none of these artists had any effect on his style, which remained unaltered throughout his career. His innumerable drawings, in various techniques of which watercolour seems to have been the favourite, have a scrupulous regard for accuracy which makes them of particular value as historical documents. His line may have something of the dry precision of an architect's tracing, but this is relieved by his feeling for the picturesque, by his precise observation of minute details and by the sense of atmosphere which he conveys with the clear light of his transparent washes.

Collectors have always appreciated Nicolle's drawings. There are important groups of them in French public collections, especially in the Louvre, the Musée Carnavalet and the Bibliothèque Nationale; and, outside Paris, in the museums of Rouen and Lille.

142 VIEW OF THE PONT-NEUF
* FROM ONE OF THE 'OEIL-DE-BOEUF' WINDOWS OF THE LOUVRE

Watercolour over pen and brown ink. The stonework surround of the window is simulated by being drawn on a separate piece of paper, cut out so as to frame the view.

508 × 394 mm

Paris, Musée Carnavalet (D. 5977)

Provenance: Bérard (sale, 1891, 16–20 February, lot 516); Decloux (sale, 1898, 14–15 February, lot 118); bought by the Musée Carnavalet in 1899.

Literature: Boucher, 1923, p. 104; the same, 1925, p. 105; *Trois siècles de dessin parisien*, exh. Paris (Musée Carnavalet) 1946, no. 275; *Dessins parisiens du* XIXè *et* XXè *siècles*, exh. Paris (Musée Carnavalet), 1976, no. 101, repr.

Signed in pen, lower right: *V. J. Nicol* and at the bottom of the window-opening: *V. J. Nicolle.*

Nicolle made many watercolours, but this one is exceptional both for its size and for the originality of its composition. The documentary accuracy which marks this artist's work is given an added charm by his feeling for space and light, which looks forward to the landscape of the Romantic period. The drawing can be dated *c.* 1810: in the foreground can be seen the yard used by the builders engaged on the colonnade of the Louvre, which was begun in 1808; and in the distance the reconstruction of the platform of the Pont-Neuf begun in 1810–11 for the proposed erection of an obelisk. In 1810 Nicolle was commissioned by Napoleon to paint fifty watercolours of the principal monuments of Paris as a wedding-present for the Empress Marie-Louise. These are now at Malmaison (see P. Schommer, *Monuments de Paris en 1810: 50 aquarelles originales inédites de V.-J. Nicolle*, Paris, 1961).

LOUIS-FRANÇOIS CASSAS

(*Azay-le-Feron 1756 – Versailles 1827*)

As well as being a painter, draughtsman and engraver, Cassas was an archaeologist and an architect; he was also an indefatigable traveller whose career was closely bound up with the rediscovery of the ancient civilizations of the Mediterranean and the publication of those discoveries. He early attracted the attention of Desfriches, of whom he remained a close friend (see their correspondence in *Dumesnil*, 1855, iii, pp. 200 ff.), and also of the duc de Rohan-Chabot, who had established a school of drawing in his Paris house where Cassas received instruction from Vernet, Vien, Lagrenée and Le Prince. From 1779 to 1783 he was in Italy, and it was there that he first fully developed his talent as a landscape draughtsman and his interest in the sites and monuments of Antiquity. He travelled incessantly, always drawing, and visited not only Rome and the surrounding country but Venice, Naples and Sicily, where he collaborated in Saint-Non's *Voyage pittoresque* (published 1781–6). He also went to Greece and, at the instance of the Emperor Joseph II, to Istria and Dalmatia.

On his return to Paris he was engaged by the newly appointed ambassador to the Sultan of Turkey, the comte de Choiseul-Gouffier, to accompany the embassy as draughtsman. The ambassador, who was a passionate archaeologist, was anxious to make a record of the classical sites and monuments in the Near East and Asia Minor, then under Turkish rule. The embassy arrived in Constantinople in September 1784, but Cassas did not stay there for more than a few weeks; for the next three or four years he was continually travelling, and making drawings, in the Troad, Egypt, Syria and Palestine. On his way home he made a second stay in Rome, from where he brought back more than two hundred and fifty drawings which had a considerable success. Returning to Paris for good, he gave himself up to the preparation of books describing his travels and illustrated by his drawings. These included: *Voyages pittoresques de la Syrie, de la Phénicie, de la Palestine, de la basse Egypte*, Paris, 1799 etc; *Voyage pittoresque de l'Istrie et de la Dalmatie*, 1800 etc; *Grandes Vues pittoresques des principaux sites et monuments de la Grèce, de la Sicile et . . . de Rome*, 1813. He acted as drawing-master at the Gobelins tapestry factory and also made a series of seventy-four models in cork and terracotta of the principal monuments of Antiquity for the Ecole des Beaux-Arts: these had a considerable influence on the development of the Neo-Classic movement in architecture at the beginning of the nineteenth century.

143 THE RUINS OF THE BATHS OF TITUS
* SEEN FROM THE COLOSSEUM

Pencil and black chalk.

241 × 380 mm

Ecole des Beaux-Arts (Inv. Masson 1297)

Provenance: from an album sold at the Cassas Sale, 14–16 January 1878, lot 342; J. Masson (Lugt 1494a) by whom presented in 1925.

Literature: Boucher, 1926, pp. 34 f.

Inscribed near lower edge, in black chalk, by the artist: *Vue des Termes de Titus prise du Colisée* and below: *du Colisée Temple de Minerva Medica*.

This drawing and nos. 144–5 formed part of a made-up album containing fifty-six drawings, mostly of Rome and the surrounding country but including five of Venice, three of the Isola Bella in Lake Maggiore, and one of Palermo, all in fine black chalk with the details elaborated in lead-pencil. These views, which contain no figures and which are inscribed in the artist's hand with the names of the places and monuments represented, are remarkable for their topographical accuracy. They were probably made with a view to being engraved. The fly-leaf of the album is inscribed: *Vues de Rome et des environs dessinées d'apres nature par L. F. Cassas de 1780 a 1784.* This last date is incorrect: the artist's first visit to Italy was only from 1779 to 1782.

The present drawing is of a view looking eastwards from the top of the Colosseum. On the left are the ruins of the Baths of Titus (now built over) and in the centre those of the Baths of Trajan. The small domed building on the horizon is the so-called 'Temple of Minerva Medica' (actually the Nymphaeum of the Gardens of Licinius) which still exists, without the cupola which collapsed in 1828, on a narrow strip of ground between the busy via Giolitti and the main railway line, a few hundred yards from the Stazione di Termini.

Another drawing in the same album is also of the Baths of Titus, but with the church of S. Pietro in Vincoli which would be to the left of the view in the present drawing.

144 VIEW OF ROCCAGIOVANE AND
* SAN COSIMATO
Black chalk.
265 × 385 mm
Ecole des Beaux-Arts (Inv. Masson 1297)

Provenance: as for no. 143.

Inscribed in the sky, by the artist, in black chalk: *Vue de Roca-Giovine San Cosimato*, and on a mountain in the left background: *forest*.

The village of Roccagiovane is below Vicovaro in the Tiburtine Hills, to the east of Rome. San Cosimato is a convent just outside Vicovaro, on the banks of the river Aniene (or Anio) which follows the line of the road between Tivoli and Vicovaro. Another drawing in the album is inscribed: '*Vue de l' Anio a San Cosimato*'.

145 VENICE: THE BACINO DI S. MARCO
* Black chalk.
235 × 372 mm
Paris, École des Beaux-Arts (Inv. Masson 1297)

Provenance: as for no. 143.

Inscribed in black chalk by the artist, on the island to the left: *S. Georges.*

This bird's-eye view must have been taken from the top of the campanile in the Piazza San Marco. On the left is part of the Isola di San Giorgio Maggiore and on the right, part of the Isola della Giudecca with the Palladian façade of the church of Le Zitelle. Other views of Venice are on pages 49–52 of the album.

JEAN-ANTOINE CONSTANTIN

(La Loubière, near Marseilles 1756 – Aix-en-Provence 1844)

Constantin was an essentially Provençal painter who played an important part in the development of the local school of landscape painting which grew up towards the end of the eighteenth century in the neighbourhood of Arles, Aix-en-Provence and Marseilles. After beginning his career in Marseilles as a decorator of faïence, he entered the Academy there, where he was instructed by landscape painters of the local school including J.-A. David (see no. 63). After spending six years in Italy he settled in Aix-en-Provence, where he was Director of the Academy until its suppression in 1792. His pupils there included Auguste de Forbin, Loubon and Granet. From 1792 until 1804, when he returned to Aix, he taught drawing at the Academy at Digne and painted views of that part of Provence. On his return to Aix he found that the Academy had been reorganized by Forbin, who himself had become Director General of the National Museum in Paris, a position in which he exerted himself to help Constantin by procuring commissions for him.

Constantin's landscape drawings were much sought after by local collectors. His work is represented in the museums at Aix and Marseilles, as well as in the Louvre and the Ecole des Beaux-Arts in Paris.

146 DISTANT VIEW OF THE ROADSTEAD AT MARSEILLES

Pen and brown ink and brown and grey wash, over black chalk.
627 × 915 mm
Louvre, Cabinet des Dessins (25,274)

Literature: Guiffrey-Marcel, iii, no. 2302, repr.; *Constantin*, exh. Marseilles, 1930, no. 88.

Signed lower left, in pen: *A. Constantin f.*

Presumably one of the three drawings commissioned from Constantin in 1817 through the good offices of Auguste de Forbin. The others are also in the Louvre (25,270, 25,278: Guiffrey-Marcel, iii, nos. 2307–8). Another series of landscapes in Provence together with a view of the Colosseum were acquired by the Musées Nationaux in 1826 and are now also in the Louvre (Guiffrey-Marcel, iii, nos. 2300, 2306, 2309–10).

147 THE RHONE AT ARLES

Pen and black ink and grey and black wash.
605 × 917 mm
Louvre, Cabinet des Dessins (25,272)

Literature: Guiffrey-Marcel, iii, no. 2301, repr.; *Constantin*, exh. Marseilles, 1930, no. 127.

This view, identified by Guiffrey-Marcel as one of Marseilles, is in fact of Arles: on the right can be seen the suburb of Trinquetaille with the pontoon bridge over the Rhone; on the left the principal monuments of the city, including the Roman amphitheatre, the tower of the cathedral of St Trophime and, nearer the river, the ruins of the palace of Constantine.

FRANÇOIS-XAVIER BIDAULT

(Carpentras 1758 – Montmorency 1846)

A pupil of his elder brother, Jean-Pierre-Joseph Bidault, who was a painter of flower and *genre* pictures at Lyons, François-Xavier worked at Arles and Tarascon before coming to Paris in 1783. There he frequented the society of his fellow Provençals, Joseph Vernet, Joseph-Siffred Duplessis and Jean-Honoré Fragonard. In 1785 he went to Rome, under the auspices of the French ambassador, Cardinal de Bernis, where he belonged to a circle of French landscape artists who included Nicolas-Didier Boguet, Nicolas-Antoine Taunay, César van Loo, Louis Gauffier and François-Xavier Fabre. In 1790 he returned to Paris, and exhibited regularly at the Salon from 1791 until only two years before his death. Like Valenciennes, his older contemporary, Bidault in his finished salon-pictures was one of the leading exponents of 'historic landscape'; and like Valenciennes he brought back from Italy a large number of landscape oil-sketches, which he used as the 'raw material' for his formal compositions. He was also one of the first to discover those parts of the French countryside that were to become the favourite haunts of the French painters of the later nineteenth century: the forest of Fontainebleau, Brittany, and Dauphiné (an album containing numerous views of the latter is in the museum at Carpentras: Dubled 1972, nos. 4–5, pp. 387 f.).

148 A GROUP OF TREES
*
Charcoal, heightened with white.
302 × 230 mm
Louvre, Cabinet des Dessins (RF 74)

Provenance: E. Gatteaux (Lugt 852), by whom presented in 1873.

Literature: Guiffrey-Marcel, i, no. 281, repr.

Signed in pen, lower left corner: *J. Bidault.*

The technique suggests a late rather than an early date.

GEORGES MICHEL

(Paris 1763 – Paris 1843)

The son of a market-porter, he was apprenticed at the age of twelve to a minor history painter, Leduc; but preferring artistic independence even at the cost of hardship, he soon left his master's studio. From the very first, he devoted himself to landscape. Like his friend Bruandet, he looked for his subjects exclusively in Paris and its suburbs and in the immediately surrounding country. As he once remarked: 'anyone who cannot find enough subjects for a lifetime within an area of four square leagues, is a fool who seeks the impossible but will never find it'. He particularly admired the seventeenth-century Dutch school, making copies of their pictures for the dealers and, at the request of Vivant-Denon, restoring those in the Louvre. This admiration is reflected in his own paintings, in which the landscape is reduced to a few simple elements in a narrow colour range of browns and greys, with the main emphasis often on a wide expanse of cloudy or stormy sky; it gained him the nickname 'the Ruysdael of Montmartre'.

From 1791 to 1814 he exhibited at the Salon, but his pictures made no impression. He ceased to exhibit and from 1821 onwards became a recluse. A public sale of his paintings which he organized in 1841 was a failure; two years later he died in obscurity and remained forgotten for thirty years. It was not until 1872 that he became known, thanks to an exhibition of his paintings at the Durand-Ruel Gallery in London. In the following year Alfred Sensier's catalogue of his work appeared, in which Michel is recognized as a forerunner of the Barbizon school.

149 A ROAD ON THE OUTSKIRTS OF PARIS

Black chalk, with some watercolour.
159 × 292 mm
Louvre, Cabinet des Dessins (RF 6145)

Literature: Guiffrey-Marcel, x, no. 9882; *Georges Michel*, exh. Paris (Galerie Charpentier), 1927, no. 89; *Paysagistes français du* XIXè *siècle*, exh. Paris (Orangerie), 1935, no. 88; *Le Paysage français avant l'Impressionisme*, exh. Geneva, 1937, no. 147; *Aspects de la vie à Paris au* XIXè *siècle*, exh. Paris (Louvre), 1954, no. 2; *Le Paysage de Saint-Denic, du* XVIIIè *siècle à nos jours*, exh. Saint-Denis, 1957, no. 107.

On the *verso*, in the same technique, is a drawing of a village in a flat landscape, inscribed: *Clignancourt et Plaine St Denis.*

Michel's widow told his biographer, Alfred Sensier, that she and her husband were accustomed to take a walk through the streets of Paris every afternoon: 'though he only very rarely painted from nature, he used to stop and make a drawing on a little piece of paper of any view that he found interesting. We would then return home through Montmartre. In this way he made hundreds and hundreds of little sketches'. The public sale of his own work which Michel organized in 1841, two years before his death, included about two thousand drawings. In 1892 the Louvre acquired two albums containing forty-eight small black chalk sketches of Paris and its suburbs (RF 1758 and 1759).

150 THE SLOPES OF MONTMARTRE
*

Black chalk and watercolour.
145 × 300 mm
Louvre, Cabinet des Dessins (RF 29,732)

Provenance: M. Gobin, from whom purchased in 1949.

Literature: Donations et Acquisitions, exh. Paris (Louvre), 1955, no. 21; Sérullaz, 1970, pl. xix.

On the *verso* is a sketch in the same technique of the church of St Pierre in Montmartre.

The influence of the Dutch seventeenth-century masters on Michel's paintings has often been remarked; in a drawing like this one he seems also to be indebted to the Dutch draughtsmen of the period, and especially perhaps to Cuyp.

FRANCOIS-MARIUS GRANET

(Aix-en-Provence 1775 – Ais-en-Provence 1849)

Granet was first influenced in the direction of landscape by J.-A. Constantin (cf. nos. 146–7), his master at the Free Drawing School at Aix; there he also met Count Auguste de Forbin (1777–1841), a fellow-pupil two years his junior, who was to become his lifelong friend and, eventually, protector. After taking part in the siege of Toulon (1793) as a draughtsman, Granet came to Paris and entered the studio of David. The rigour of the Neo-Classic school was less to his taste than the example of the Dutch and Flemish seventeenth-century masters, and the title of the first picture that he exhibited at the Salon, *Interior of a cloister* (1799), shows that the lines of his future development were fixed even before he and Forbin went to Rome in 1802. Granet remained there until 1819, when the success at the Salon of his *Choir of the Capuchin Church* (Hermitage, Leningrad) decided him to return to Paris. He had already made his reputation with his first important painting, *Jacques Stella in prison* (Pushkin Museum, Moscow), exhibited at the Salon in 1810. In 1813 he was elected to the Academia di San Luca. His circle in Rome included Ingres, whose portrait of him, painted in 1807 and now in the Musée Granet at Aix, is one of his early masterpieces. In the pictures that Granet himself painted for exhibition, his preference was for subjects of ruins and interiors of churches and monasteries, vaulted rooms, cells and dungeons, often peopled with monks; but true to the tradition of French artists in Italy, he made many drawings and oil-sketches of the landscape of Rome and its surroundings.

On his return to Paris in 1819 he found Forbin established as Director General of the French Museums, and through his influence was in 1826 given a curatorship at the Louvre. In 1830, King Louis-Philippe, who had seized the throne after the July Revolution, entrusted him with the organization of the Museum of French History which he intended to establish at Versailles. It was during this period that Granet executed the beautiful series of watercolour views of the park at Versailles (Louvre and Musée Granet at Aix), in which the same subjects are represented at different times of day and in different conditions of light. After Louis-Philippe's fall from power in 1848 Granet retired to Aix-en-Provence. He bequeathed to the Louvre one hundred and ninety-nine of his drawings, chosen by himself; and to his native city the rest of the contents of his studio (including the oil sketches) and his collections, in which the most conspicuous object was the portrait by Ingres.

151 THE ARCH OF CONSTANTINE FROM
* THE COLOSSEUM

Black chalk and grey wash.
436 × 305 mm
Louvre, Cabinet des Dessins (26,812)

Provenance: bequeathed by the artist in 1849.

Literature: Guiffrey-Marcel, vi, no. 4411; *Artistes français en Italie de Poussin à Renoir*, exh. Paris (Musée des Arts Decoratifs), 1934, no. 512; *Monuments et sites d'Italie vus par les dessinateurs français de Callot à Degas*, exh. Paris (Louvre), 1958, no. 58; *François-Marius Granet*, exh. Paris (Louvre), 1960, no. 4.

Numbered in pen, lower left: *65*.

In his *Recollections* (manuscript in the Musée Arbaud at Aix; published in *Le Temps*, 28 September–28 October 1872) Granet described his first impressions of Rome in 1802: 'After exploring the whole city, I decided to begin by making some studies from nature. As my first subject, I chose the Colosseum, a monument that had particularly struck me because of its extraordinary shape and the masses of vegetation that clothed its ruins, and the enchanting effect that it produced against the sky'. The present drawing, which must date from the beginning of Granet's stay in Rome, is of the Arch of Constantine seen through one of the arcaded openings of the Colosseum. At the Salon of 1806 Granet exhibited an *Interior view of the Colosseum*, bought in the same year by the Louvre (Sterling-

Adhémar, ii, 1959, no. 987, repr.). Two studies for this picture are in the Cabinet des Dessins of the Louvre (26,810 and 26,811), and there is another view of the galleries of the Colosseum in the museum at Dijon (*Dessins de la collection His de la Salle*, exh. Dijon, 1974, no. 72, repr.).

152 IMPRESSION OF ROME AT SUNSET

Brown wash.

215 × 340 mm

Louvre, Cabinet des Dessins (26,803)

Provenance: bequeathed by the artist in 1849.

Literature: Guiffrey-Marcel, vi, no. 4401; *French Art*, exh. London (Royal Academy), 1932, no. 858 (Commemorative Catalogue, no. 852); *Artistes français en Italie de Poussin à Renoir*, exh. Paris (Musée des Arts Decoratifs), 1934, no. 510; *Monuments et sites d'Italie vus par les dessinateurs français de Callot à Degas*, exh. Paris (Louvre), 1958, no. 60; *Maîtres du Blanc et Noir*, exh. Rennes, 1972, and Dijon, 1975, no. 10, repr.

Inscribed on the *verso*, in black chalk: *le dôme de San Carlo al Corso* and on the back of the old mount, in pen: *Souvenir pris sur place de la Trinité de Mont à Rome, au moment où le soleil vient de descendre à l'horizon. Le Dôme est celui de San Carlo al Corso.*

The word 'souvenir' shows that this is not intended as a literal view of Rome at sunset from the terrace in front of the church of S. Trinità dei Monti, at the top of the Spanish Steps. The drawing is in fact a generalized impression – one could almost call it a *capriccio* – composed of elements from various parts of Rome: to the left of the cupola of S. Carlo al Corso are the Antonine Column, the dome of the Pantheon, and the Torre delle Milizie; while the slope on the right is presumably intended to be Monte Mario. Chateaubriand indulged in reverie on the same spot, at the same sunset hour: 'from outside S. Trinità dei Monti the distant towers and buildings seem like a painter's partly rubbed-out sketch, or a view from the sea of an irregular line of cliffs'. Granet imparts something of the same poetic quality to his drawing by his atmospheric use of freely handled brown wash – a reversion to the practice of the 'Italianizing' draughtsmen of the seventeenth century, such as Breenbergh and Claude Lorrain, and in striking contrast to the drily linear technique of the Neo-Classic followers of David (e.g. nos. 153–5).

ACHILLE-ETNA MICHALLON
(Paris 1796 – Paris 1822)

His father, the sculptor Claude Michallon (1751–99), died when he was three. His masters included J.-L. David and some of the leading landscape-painters of the day, Valenciennes, A.-H. Dunouy and J.-V. Bertin. A precocious pupil, he had a picture in the Salon when he was sixteen; and in 1816 the Prix de Rome for Historic Landscape was created for him, which he won in the following year with an idealized and Arcadian landscape *Democritus and the people of Abdera* (Ecole des Beaux-Arts).

The years 1817 to 1821 Michallon spent at the French Academy in Rome. The paintings of epic or tragic subjects that he sent home such as *The death of Roland*, 1819 (Louvre), *Theseus and the Centaurs*, 1821 (Louvre) and *Philoctetes at Lemnos* (Musée Fabre, Montpellier), differ from the usual kind of tranquil Neo-Classic landscape in their emphasis on sharp verticals and diagonals and their marked contrasts of light and shade. Michallon was clearly influenced by some of the German artists then active in Rome, particularly Joseph Koch (1786–1839). At the same time he produced oil-sketches in the tradition of Valenciennes, and constitutes a direct link between Valenciennes and Corot, who was a pupil in his studio during the short interval between his return to Paris and his death.

153 THE COLOSSEUM AND THE ARCH OF CONSTANTINE FROM THE PALATINE
Pencil.
285 × 429 mm
Louvre, Cabinet des Dessins (RF 13,886)

Provenance: Comte de l'Espine; Princesse Louis de Croÿ, by whom presented in 1930.

Literature: Oeuvres provenant des donations faites par Madame la Princesse Louis de Croÿ, exh. Paris (Orangerie), 1930, no. 160; *Les Artistes français en Italie*, exh. Paris (Musée des Arts Decoratifs), 1934, no. 579; *Monuments et sites d'Italie vus par les dessinateurs français de Callot à Degas*, exh. Paris (Louvre), 1958, no. 62; *Il Disegno francese dal Fouquet a Toulouse-Lautrec*, exh. Rome, 1959, no. 132; *L'Italia vista dai pittori francesi del* XVIII *e* XIX *secolo*, exh. Rome-Turin, 1961, no. 224, pl. 54; *The Age of Neo-Classicism*, exh. London (Royal Academy), 1972, no. 697.

This panoramic view, from the southern slope of the Palatine Hill, shows on the left part of the convent of S. Bonaventura and in the distance on the right the convent of S. Pietro in Vincoli; on the extreme right is the end of the Claudian Aqueduct, behind which are the Arch of Constantine and the Colosseum.

In his oil-sketches of Rome and the Campagna, Michallon, like Valenciennes before him, was above all concerned with recording the changing effects of light at different seasons of the year and times of day. In his pencil drawings, on the other hand, he followed the example of his master Bertin (and anticipated his pupil Corot) in reducing effects of light to the minimum while concentrating on the spatial relationship between the component parts of the landscape and a careful analysis of all its details.

154 THE AURELIAN WALLS, WITH THE CHURCH OF
* S. CROCE IN GERUSALEMME IN THE DISTANCE
Black chalk.
292 × 429 mm
Louvre, Cabinet des Dessins (RF 14,880)

Provenance: as for no. 153.

155 THE ROAD FROM TIVOLI TO SUBIACO
Black chalk.
295 × 437 mm
Louvre, Cabinet des Dessins (RF 14,254)

Provenance: as for no. 153.

Literature: L'Italia vista dai pittori francesi del XVIII *e* XIX *secolo*, exh. Rome-Turin, 1961, no. 223.

Inscribed in black chalk, lower left, evidently by the artist: *route de Tivoli à Subiaco 2*.

1 Patel   *270 × 406 mm*

3 Silvestre   *392 × 889 mm*

7 Desportes *300 × 530 mm*

9 Desportes *310 × 510 mm*

12 Desportes   *295 × 500 mm*

Desportes   *365 × 530 mm*

21 Watteau 215 × 303 mm

22 Oudry   *198 × 255 mm*
◄27 Oudry   *325 × 472 mm*

6 Oudry   *386 × 527 mm*

Dans les Jardins de M. Crozat à Montmorenci. 1724.

30 Mariette   *401 × 267 mm*

31 Portail *272 × 421 mm*

28 Oudry *305 × 525 mm*

41 Pierre *196 × 257 mm*

39 Boucher *353 × 479 mm*

42 Vernet   *262 × 379 mm*

44 Vernet   *294 × 430 mm*

47 Blarenberghe   *441 × 1390 mm*

56 Challe   *326 × 460 mm*

59 Clérisseau   *265 × 382 mm*

62 Saint-Aubin   *371 × 538 mm*

68 Pérignon   *243 × 385 mm*

70 Pillement   *383 × 550 mm*

73 Lantara   *238 × 345 mm*

64 Le Mettay   *294 × 457 mm*

75 Volaire *256 × 505 mm*

76 Amand *294 × 422 mm*

84 Fragonard *456 × 347 mm*

79 Fragonard *350 × 487 mm*

87 Robert   *453 × 352 mm*
◀81 Fragonard   *348 × 482 mm*

86 Robert *294 × 435 mm*

89 Robert *123 × 220 mm*

91 Robert *170 × 225 mm*
◀92 Robert *392 × 532 mm*

97 Le Prince *230 × 295 mm*

93 Robert *750 × 980 mm*

121 Saint-Morys *115 × 166 mm*

123 Suvée *324 × 445 mm*

134

98 Lespinasse *290 × 625 mm*

122 Desprez 416 × 900 mm

99 Lespinasse *480 × 991 mm*

100 Lespinasse   *517 × 1000 mm*

137

4 Van der Meulen   *285 × 408 mm*

35 Natoire   *290 × 471 mm*

107 Houel *285 × 483 mm*

106 Houel *302 × 483 mm*

101 Houel 265 × 435 mm

108 Houel 298 × 454 mm

109 Houel   *290 × 421 mm*

110 Houel   *288 × 428 mm*

120 Moreau *356 × 541 mm*

137 Valenciennes   *172 × 260 mm*

138 Valenciennes   *256 × 381 mm*

◀135 Valenciennes   *260 × 383 mm*

128 David   *150 × 216 mm*

112 Houel   *298 × 430 mm*

130 Valenciennes   *95 × 273 mm*

131 Valenciennes   *263 × 404 mm*

126 Norblin de la Gourdaine   *340 × 420 mm*

143 Cassas   *241 × 380 mm*

144 Cassas   *265 × 385 mm*

142 Nicolle   *508 × 394 mm*

149 Michel   *159 × 292 mm*

150 Michel   *145 × 300 mm*

148 Bidault *302 × 230 mm*

151 Granet   *436 × 305 mm*

145 Cassas *235 × 372 mm*

154 Michallon *292 × 429 mm*